SSMG

HEINEMANN MATHEMATICS 8
Teacher's Notes

For England and Wales . . .

Heinemann Mathematics and the National Curriculum

Heinemann Mathematics 7, 8 and 9 together are suitable for pupils working at levels 4, 5 and 6 of the National Curriculum.

	HM7	HM8	HM9
NC level	3 4 5 6 7		

For Scotland . . .

Heinemann Mathematics and Mathematics 5–14

Heinemann Mathematics, 7, 8 and 9 together are suitable for pupils working at levels D and E of the Mathematics 5–14 programme in Scotland.

	HM7	HM8	HM9
5–14 level	D E E+		

For Northern Ireland . . .

Heinemann Mathematics and the Common Curriculum

Heinemann Mathematics 7, 8 and 9 together are suitable for pupils working at levels 4, 5 and 6 of the Common Curriculum in Northern Ireland.

	HM7	HM8	HM9
CC level	4 5 6 7		

PREFACE

These notes are an integral and essential part of Heinemann Mathematics. As well as a general introduction to the course and a description of its structure, the notes provide the following detailed information for each section of work.

- Structure maps to show the links between Core, Support and Extension
- Mathematical Content and Development
- References to the National Curriculum and Mathematics 5–14 Guidelines
- Equipment required
- Suggestions for Related, Introductory and Additional activities.
- Detailed comments and suggestions concerning particular questions.

AUTHORS
John T. Blair
Kenneth V. Carpy
Ian K. Clark
John B. Dalton
Percy W. Farren
Douglas H. Goodall
Peter S. Henderson
Ian S. Jones
Thomas J. Sanaghan
Dorothy S. Simpson

Heinemann Educational Publishers
Halley Court, Jordan Hill, Oxford OX2 8EJ
a division of Reed Educational & Professional Publishing Ltd

MELBOURNE AUCKLAND FLORENCE PRAGUE MADRID
ATHENS SINGAPORE TOKYO SAO PAULO
CHICAGO PORTSMOUTH (NH) MEXICO IBADAN
GABORONE JOHANNESBURG KAMPALA NAIROBI

ISBN 0 435 03950 4

© Scottish Primary Mathematics Group 1992

First published 1992

Revised edition 1995
97 98 5 4

Designed and produced by VAP Group, Kidlington, Oxon.

Printed and bound by Athenæum Press Ltd., Gateshead, Tyne & Wear.

CONTENTS

INTRODUCTION TO THE COURSE

The complete Heinemann Mathematics course aims to provide a programme of mathematics for pupils aged from 5 to 16.

The materials that comprise Heinemann Mathematics 7, 8 and 9 are suitable for pupils working at

- Levels 4, 5 and 6 of the National Curriculum (England and Wales)
- Levels D and E of the Mathematics 5 – 14 programme in Scotland
- Levels 4, 5 and 6 of the Common Curriculum (Northern Ireland).

Work is provided in relation to all the Attainment Targets in the above curricula at the Levels indicated with the exception of those Attainment Targets concerned with using computers.

The provision of Support material for less-able pupils and Extension material for more-able pupils is designed to ensure that, on completion of Heinemann Mathematics 9, Key Stage 3 pupils in England, Wales and Northern Ireland can demonstrate their ability to work at Level 5 or Level 6 or to some extent Level 7. The differentiated nature of the materials should also enable each pupil to embark on the appropriate level of GCSE or Standard Grade course at the appropriate time.

Some of the mathematical work in Heinemann Mathematics 7 was first published as part of *Mathematics: a development through activity* by Scottish Primary Mathematics Group. This has been extensively revised and restructured by a combined group of authors from SPMG and SSMG (Scottish Secondary Mathematics Group). Heinemann Mathematics 8 and 9 contain new material from SSMG whose aim has been to consolidate and build upon the most widely used mathematics programme in primary schools.

Rationale

Development

Pupils' understanding of mathematics should be progressive. As their course develops they should gain an overview of mathematics which is both wide and coherent and which goes well beyond the bare requirements set out in any list of attainment targets whether national or local. Clearly such progression is more readily obtained when care is taken to link new ideas directly with those previously encountered. The work for pupils throughout Heinemann Mathematics has been written with the need to ensure this progression to the fore. At the same time there is sufficient flexibility in the design of the materials to allow teachers and pupils to vary their route through the mathematics.

Continuity

Pupils' progress in mathematics should not be hindered by a lack of continuity, for example in resources or materials, in the use of mathematical language or in the teaching approaches adopted. Heinemann Mathematics addresses the needs of pupils throughout their schooling and thus contributes positively to a continuity of experience which in the past has often proved difficult to achieve, particularly when pupils move from primary to secondary school. Examples of *Teaching Approaches* applied throughout Heinemann Mathematics are given on page T2.

Activity

Pupils should experience mathematics in an active and practical way. The use of both structured and non-structured apparatus and the use of diagrams and pictures to help pupils acquire concepts and understand techniques is encouraged throughout Heinemann Mathematics. Practical work is advocated to secure concepts, develop meaningful language and to allow pupils to use and apply their mathematics.

Calculators

In our technologically-based society pupils are familiar, from an early age, with the use of calculators for computation. Calculators feature in Heinemann Mathematics with the intention that pupils should learn to use them intelligently. However, in different situations which necessitate computation, pupils should be able to use methods of calculation appropriate to these situations. Accordingly pupils are frequently expected to use paper-and-pencil methods as well as mental calculation.

Investigation

Pupils should be able to use their mathematics – facts, concepts, skills and thinking processes – to solve problems and to investigate. Throughout Heinemann Mathematics pupils are given opportunities to tackle problems – practical, real-life and mathematical – and it is recommended that topics are approached in an investigative way.

Contextualisation

Pupils should experience the use of mathematics in a wide variety of contexts including some which are cross-curricular in nature. Opportunities for demonstrating the important place of mathematics across the curriculum, in everyday life, in employment and in leisure – are virtually endless. An important feature of Heinemann Mathematics is the widespread presentation of mathematical ideas in contexts which are relevant to the pupils' world. Such contexts are more likely to stimulate their interest in mathematics and encourage positive attitudes.

Teaching Approaches

Pupils who have not in their earlier mathematical work made use of Heinemann Mathematics or the SPMG course but have been following a programme of study as described in any of the national curricula should be able to enter the Heinemann Mathematics course at any stage with confidence. There follows a description of teaching approaches used in earlier stages of Heinemann Mathematics or the SPMG course which are built upon in Heinemann Mathematics 7, 8 and 9 to give continuity of experience.

Problem Solving and Investigation

Many opportunities have been provided for the pupils to learn through practical activity, to apply mathematics to real-life problems and to explore and investigate mathematical ideas. They should have gradually developed an awareness of problem solving as a process in three broad steps, namely: getting started, doing the work, and reporting to others. The pupils' experiences of problem solving and investigation have been planned to

- allow them to use their mathematical knowledge and skills in new and unfamiliar situations
- develop their awareness of ideas of argument and proof
- develop their ability to communicate in mathematics.

Some of the work may be tackled at an individual level, particularly where it occurs among other examples on Core Textbook or Workbook pages. It is also beneficial on many occasions for problem solving to be carried out in pairs or in small groups of perhaps three or four pupils learning for themselves and from each other.

A systematic treatment of a range of stategies for problem solving is presented across Heinemann Mathematics 7, 8 and 9. These strategies are unlikely to be developed formally by the pupils for themselves and it is expected that they will require separate teaching.

Number

A consistent approach has been applied when developing written techniques for the four operations:

- concrete materials such as structured base ten apparatus are manipulated to arrive at a result
- when manipulating these materials emphasis is placed on establishing an appropriate language
- the manipulation of materials and the appropriate language are then linked to a written technique
- practice is provided to consolidate the written technique.

Subtraction

The method of subtraction which arises naturally from the manipulation of materials is *decomposition*. The following example illustrates a written technique which reflects the way the materials are manipulated and indicates the accompanying language.

$$
\begin{array}{ccc}
T & U & \cdot & t \\
{}^{3}\!\!\!/\!\!4 & {}^{14}\!\!\!/\!\!5 & \cdot & {}^{1}3 \\
-\ 1 & 6 & \cdot & 7 \\
\hline
2 & 8 & \cdot & 6 \\
\end{array}
$$

7 tenths from 3 tenths. I cannot do this. Exchange 1 unit for 10 tenths to give 4 units and 13 tenths. 7 tenths from 13 tenths leaves 6 tenths.

6 units from 4 units. I cannot do this. Exchange 1 ten for 10 units to give 3 tens and 14 units. 6 units from 14 units leaves 8 units.

1 ten from 3 tens leaves 2 tens.

Division

The following example illustrates a written technique which reflects the process of *sharing* materials and indicates the accompanying language.

$$
\begin{array}{ccc}
 & T & U & \cdot & t \\
 & 2 & 5 & \cdot & 3 \\
3\overline{)} & 7 & {}^{1}6 & \cdot & {}^{1}5 \\
\end{array}
$$

Share the 7 tens. 7 shared equally among 3 (or divided by 3) is 2, rem 1.

Share the 16 units. 16 shared equally among 3 is 5, rem 1.

Share the 15 tenths. 15 shared equally among 3 is 5.

When pupils encounter a word problem involving *grouping* language, as they frequently do, they must first establish that division is required and then use the technique illustrated above to find the result.

For division by a two-digit number pupils use a process of successive subtractions as follows. The accompanying language reflects the *context* of the problem, whether grouping or sharing is implied.

2549 cans of cola are to be packed in boxes each holding 12 cans. How many full boxes will there be? How many cans will be left over?

$$
\begin{array}{rrl}
2549 & & \leftarrow 2549 \text{ cans to be packed.} \\
-1200 & 100 & \leftarrow\ 100 \text{ boxes use 1200 cans. } (100 \times 12 = 1200) \\
\hline
1349 & & \leftarrow 1349 \text{ cans are left.} \\
-1200 & 100 & \leftarrow\ 100 \text{ boxes use 1200 cans. } (100 \times 12 = 1200) \\
\hline
149 & & \leftarrow\ 149 \text{ cans are left.} \\
-120 & 10 & \leftarrow\ 10 \text{ boxes use 120 cans. } \quad (10 \times 12 = 120) \\
\hline
29 & & \leftarrow\ 29 \text{ cans are left.} \\
-12 & 1 & \leftarrow\ 1 \text{ box uses 12 cans. } \quad (1 \times 12 = 12) \\
\hline
17 & & \leftarrow\ 17 \text{ cans are left.} \\
-12 & 1 & \leftarrow\ 1 \text{ box uses 12 cans. } \quad (1 \times 12 = 12) \\
\hline
5 & \underline{212} & \\
\end{array}
$$

There will be 212 full boxes. 5 cans will be left over.

In general division by two (or more)-digit numbers is likely to be by calculator. Hence an emphasis is placed on its efficient use and on interpretation of the display.

Other methods

There are many situations in which the use of a standard written technique may not be the most appropriate method of computation. Pupils are expected to use alternative methods – written, mental and calculator – and to choose the most appropriate method for the computation in hand. Examples include:

- subtraction by 'counting on' when calculating change and when finding time differences
- mental multiplication and division by 10 and by 100
- mental estimation using single-digit rounding to check the reasonableness of a calculator result or a money total at a supermarket checkout.

Measure

The emphasis in the teaching approach to measure is very much on practical work. Nevertheless, written examples are also provided in each aspect of measure – length, weight, area, volume and time. Practical work is designed to secure concepts, give practice in measuring skills and develop language. Much of the content is presented within contexts so that learning is related to real-life situations.

The aspects of measure are developed along the following lines albeit at different rates:

- comparing and ordering experiences to develop relationships and associated language
- the use of arbitrary standards (for example, spans or cupfuls) to quantify measure and to show the need for an agreed standard measure
- the use of standard measures (for example, metres or litres) in estimating and measuring activities
- the use of fractional parts of these standard measures, leading to an awareness of the approximate nature of measure, that is, an awareness that any measurement is made to a selected degree of accuracy.

Although most measurements are carried out in metric standard units, Imperial units are also used where they are still in common use, for example, feet and inches for heights, miles for distances and gallons for volumes.

Shape and Position

The emphasis is again on practical work. From an early stage informal practical activities are used to develop the pupils' abilities to recognise shapes and their awareness of some properties of shapes. Pupils handle, examine, sort and build three-dimensional shapes. They cut out, fit, move, fold, sort and examine two-dimensional shapes. Plasticine, card, paper, nailboards and Meccano-type strips are used to make shapes. As the pupils' measuring skills develop and they explore real-life situations, work in Shape and Measure are integrated, for example, formulae for the area of a triangle and the volume of a cuboid are applied.

The aesthetic and recreational appeal of working with patterns of coloured shapes, tessellations, shape puzzles, curve stitching, symmetrical shapes and so on is powerful and can have positive effects on the pupils' view of mathematics in general. Pupils who experience difficulty for example, in Number work, can often gain confidence through their achievements in Shape work.

Handling data

The pupils' experiences of handling data and information are already wide and have been developed progressively. In providing work to develop the relevant concepts and skills emphasis is placed on

- collecting data: this involves pupils in identifying data they wish to collect as well as designing observation sheets and carrying out practical surveys
- organising data: this develops from simple sorting activities to the use of 'tick' sheets and later more sophisticated frequency tables requiring pupils to choose suitable class intervals
- displaying data: methods of display progress from the use of real objects and the use of pictures to the construction of a wide range of graphs; pupils are made aware of relative strengths and weaknesses of different forms of graphs and are asked to select the most appropriate form for given data and their own data
- interpreting data: this involves pupils in answering questions about a given graph as well as devising questions about graphs they themselves have constructed.

In addition, other resources such as computer databases and graph-plotting packages should continue to be used to expand and develop the pupils' experience of handling data.

STRUCTURE OF THE COURSE

Format

Material is provided at three levels:

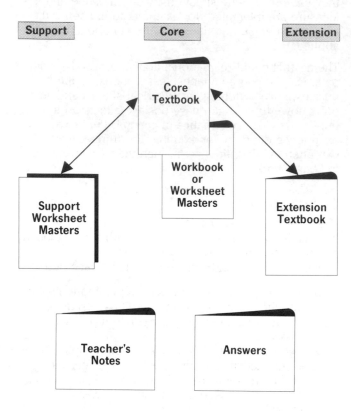

Core Textbook and Workbook

The Core material comprises a Textbook and an associated Workbook (which is also available as photocopiable Worksheet Masters). The Textbook is divided into four parts which should be tackled in the order in which they appear. Each *Part* contains a number of sections covering different aspects of mathematics. Within each *Part* the order in which sections are tackled is not important, allowing flexibility in planning programmes of study. The top of each Textbook page contains the following information:

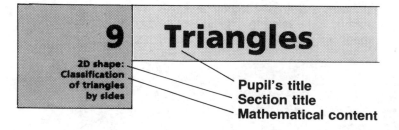

Pupil's title
Section title
Mathematical content

Workbook pages are used in conjunction with the Core Textbook. This expendable material is designed to avoid pupils spending unnecessary amounts of time copying tables, diagrams and graphs. It also provides templates for cut-out shapes and, on occasions, a structured layout to help develop recording skills.

The following symbols and instructions appear on the pages:

 indicated the use of associated Workbook material

Go back to Textbook . . . refers pupils back to the appropriate Core Textbook reference

Ask your teacher what to do next.
indicates the end of a section.

Support

This material is provided in the form of photocopiable Worksheet Masters, although on occasions pupils are directed to answer some questions in their jotters (copy books, exercise books). Not every section of the Core Textbook has associated Support work. Where experience suggests that some pupils may have difficulty progressing far in the Core material, Support work is provided in one of two forms.

- Lead-in work is at a simpler level to that of the Core, designed to provide preparatory work related to the Core.
- Parallel work contains similar content to that of the Core but is set at a simpler level, in less demanding contexts and develops ideas more slowly.

 indicates that the questions should be answered in jotters.

Extension

In the Extension Textbook material is provided related to certain sections. In general, in Heinemann Mathematics 7 and 8 little new work is introduced, rather the contexts in which the work is set become more demanding. However, in Heinemann Mathematics 9, much of the Extension introduces new content to provide able pupils with the necessary grounding for the most demanding levels of the Standard Grade and GCSE courses. Answers are supplied in the back of the Extension Textbook.

Answer Book

Answers to Support and Core work only are supplied in a single book.

Teacher's Notes

Throughout this book the following abbreviations are used to refer to other pupil component pages:

- (just page number) – Core Textbook
- W (+ page number) – Workbook
- S (+ page number) – Support
- E (+ page number) – Extension

Class Organisation

The material has been designed and written to cope with the demands of teaching to mixed ability or set classes. It is flexible in its application and can be used to support a variety of different forms of class organisation:

- whole class
- groups, ability or social
- individuals.

All these forms of class organisation have their place, and indeed there are real benefits to be gained from varying the organisation to suit different situations.

Whatever form of class organisation is used, the material gives teachers the opportunity to teach, and indeed the need for a positive, regular input from teachers is paramount.

More detailed advice on class organisation is given in the section *Using the Course in the Classroom* and in the detailed page-by-page notes for each section.

Using the Course in the Classroom

Preparation

It is important that the teacher takes the time to read the Teacher's Notes for each section of work before teaching that section. These notes provide valuable information in the form of a Section Overview and a set of Page-by-Page Notes.

Section Overview

- Structure map showing the relationship among Core, Support and Extension
- Content and Development detailing assumed knowledge and the work of the section
- National Curricula references showing how the work contributes to the pupils' experience of the individual Attainment Targets
- Equipment list indicating the requirements for the section
- Related activities to complement the work of the section.

Page-by-Page Notes

- National Curricula references showing how the work of the page contributes to the pupils' experience of the individual Attainment Targets
- Content detailing the mathematical ideas contained on the page
- Equipment list indicating the requirements for the page
- Organisation where a particular teaching approach is required or recommended
- Introductory activities suggesting possible teaching approaches
- Detailed advice referring to specific questions
- Additional activities suggesting possible follow-up work.

Beginning a Section of Work

It is anticipated that most if not all the pupils in a class will begin a section of work at the same time, giving the opportunity for introductory teaching, scene-setting activities and discussion, possibly making use of the suggested introductory activities. As the work develops it is likely that pupils will progress at different rates, giving rise to the formation of a small number of groups.

It may be appropriate for some pupils to be directed to Support material early in the section and for some of the more able pupils to be given Extension work at the end of the section. In this way teaching and discussion can be directed effectively either to the whole class, to a group of pupils or to individuals as appropriate. The class should come together again to begin the next section of work.

Routes Through a Section

A description of the relationship among Core, Support and Extension pages and a diagram showing this relationship and possible routes through each section are given in the Teacher's Notes for each section. The most likely route is indicated in the structure map by continuous lines. Alternative routes are indicated by dotted lines. An example is given below.

Although most pupils may be capable of making a start in the Core Textbook, the teacher may wish certain pupils to begin with the Support materials. It is neither necessary nor desirable for every pupil to do all the work on every page. A balanced selection of work should be made according to the pupils' abilities.

S10	S11	S12
Completing tables	Extending tables	Using patterns

23 W6 W7	24 W8	25	26, 27
$y = ax$	$y = ax + b$	$y = ax$, $y = ax + b$	Coordinate patterns

E4	E5	E6
From patterns	Introducing symbols	Finding a formula

Teaching

The materials must not be regarded as a programmed text. Preliminary teaching is generally necessary before the pupils attempt the Textbook and Workbook pages. Moreover, although the Textbook and Workbook pages do include brief instructions and explanations, it is essential that the teacher reads and discusses these with the pupils to ensure that they are fully understood before the pupils proceed with the work.

Special Features

Symbols

 This symbol appears alongside some questions, often at the end of certain pages, and indicates that these questions are of a more demanding nature.

 Certain sections and whole pages are devoted to investigative work. This symbol has been used to identify questions which provide additional opportunities for pupils to develop and use problem solving skills.

 This symbol indicates a reminder of key information essential for the work of the page.

Detours

A **Detour** is designed to widen the mathematical experience of the pupils. **Detours** are presented as single pages of work distributed throughout Heinemann Mathematics 7, 8 and 9. They provide work which is important and worthwhile but which is not necessarily related to the work of a specific area of content. The work in the **Detours** often requires an exploratory, investigative approach which draws upon the pupils' problem solving skills. In many cases the topics lend themselves to further development.

Detours are provided at Support, Core and Extension levels and form a pool of self-contained activities which can be dipped into from time to time. They can be used in different ways, for example

- by individuals or groups who have completed their set work early
- by a group or whole class to provide a change of focus in their work
- to provide, on occasions, additional problem solving activities and challenges.

The **Detours** should *not* be attempted as though they form a single section of work. However, for convenience, The Teacher's Notes for the **Detours** within each part have been grouped together and placed at the end of the Notes for that *Part*.

Extended Contexts

Contexts are used throughout Heinemann Mathematics to present and develop mathematical ideas. A context may feature on a single Textbook or Workbook page; sometimes the theme is continued on two or more pages. An **Extended context**, however, deals with the same theme over a whole section of the course.

There are two extended contexts at each stage containing simulated activities which form the basis for developing mathematical work which is real in its usefulness and application. Most of the mathematical concepts and skills involved are familiar to the pupils although some may only have been recently developed.

In organising and managing the work of the **Extended context** the teacher should consider the following principles:

- The **Extended context** need not be tackled as a continuous piece of work. Some teachers may choose to enhance the on-going mathematics programme by dipping into the **Extended context** from time to time.
- The contexts include many activities which can be attempted by *all* pupils. However, since there is work for pupils of different levels of ability it is advised that pupils should, on many occasions, work in groups. These can be formed on the basis of similar ability, mixed ability or social considerations.
- It is almost certain that no pupils will attempt every activity. It is likely that some groups will omit a part or parts of a context. Also, different groups may work simultaneously on separate aspects of a context.

It is important, therefore, that at appropriate times, when group activity has been completed, a full class discussion of the work done takes place. Pupils should report orally to others; they should be asked to write about their work, to explain results, and to interpret diagrams and graphs which have been produced. Wall displays should be mounted. Part of the teacher's role is to maximise the involvement of *all* the pupils in the work of the context, either directly in carrying out the suggested activities, or indirectly through discussion of the work of others.

Progress Records

A number of items are offered to help teachers record the progress of their pupils.

- A **Record of Work Grid**
- **Pupil Progress Records** linked to the National Curriculum (England and Wales) and the Mathematics 5–14 Guidelines (Scotland).
- A **Class Progress Record**.

A full description can be found on page T12.

References to Attainment Targets

Detailed references to attainment targets for the National Curriculum (England and Wales) and the Mathematics 5–14 Guidelines (Scotland) are included in these Teacher's Notes in both the Section Overview and the Page-by-Page Notes. These references are provided as an aid to planning and recording. There is no intention to suggest that teaching should follow the targets in a slavish way.

A summary of the coverage of Heinemann Mathematics 8 is given for the National Curriculum (England and Wales) on page T28 and for the Mathematics 5–14 Guidelines on page T30. In each summary chart, a blank space indicates coverage of work towards a particular attainment target or strand.

England and Wales

■ The Teacher's Notes contain detailed references to the Programme of Study statements within the four Attainment Targets at Key Stage 3. The following code is used to identify the Attainment Targets:

Using and Applying Mathematics	**UA**	Shape, Space and Measure	**SM**
Number	**N**	Handling Data	**HD**
Algebra	**A**		

The referencing shows each Attainment Target, Programme of Study Section and Subsection, and NC Level. For example:

Number
Attainment   **N3d/6** ———— NC Level 6
Target

Programme of Study Section 3   Subsection d

(Understand when and how to use fractions and percentages to make proportional comparisons)

■ Some of the outcomes specified in the Programme of Study statements relate to skills or concepts which children develop over an extended period. In these circumstances the NC Level is sometimes indicated by an arrow. For example:

$$N3d/5 \rightarrow 6$$

refers to Number work appropriate to children at Level 5 "working towards" a statement which is at Level 6 in the Level Descriptions.

■ The work in a section or single page of Heinemann Mathematics 8 frequently relates to more than one Section or Subsection of the Programme of Study. On these occasions, for economy of presentation, statements at the same Level for the Attainment Target are combined. For example:

$$N3de, 4a/5$$

■ Within each Attainment Target, Programme of Study Section 1 overarches all the other Sections. As the Heinemann Mathematics course includes coverage of all the statements in these other Sections, separate references to Section 1 statements are not made.

Scotland

In the Mathematics 5–14 Guidelines, the strands within each attainment outcome are not numbered or lettered. We have therefore devised a system of referencing using a code based on the initial letter(s) of each strand and the appropriate level. The coding is as follows:

Number, Money and Measurement	Code	Shape, Position and Movement	Code
Range and Type of Numbers	**RTN**	Range of Shapes	**RS**
Money	**M**	Position and Movement	**PM**
Add and Subtract	**AS**	Symmetry	**S**
Multiply and Divide	**MD**	Angle	**A**
Round Numbers	**RN**		
Fractions, Percentages and Ratio	**FPR**	**Problem-Solving and Enquiry**	**PSE**
Patterns and Sequences	**PS**	**Information Handling**	
Functions and Equations	**FE**	Collect	**C**
Measure and Estimate	**ME**	Organise	**O**
Time	**T**	Display	**D**
Perimeter, Formulae, Scales	**PFS**	Interpret	**I**

The referencing shows strand code, level and attainment target. For example:

MD/E2 ———— Second target

Multiply and Divide   Level E   (Multiply and divide mentally for any numbers including decimals by 10, 100, 1000 in applications in number, measurement and money.)

On occasion the referencing indicates only the strand code and level. This occurs when the attainment targets do not provide an adequate description of the work.

Work beyond Level E is indicated using E+.
Where E+ appears alongside other references then an element of the work is at that level.
Where E+ appears on its own then all of the work is at that level.

Northern Ireland

References to the Common Curriculum (Northern Ireland) are coded as in the published curriculum.

HEINEMANN MATHEMATICS 8

Equipment

Basic equipment

The following is assumed to be normally available.

Paper: A4 plain, 2 mm, ½ cm, and 1 cm squared, 1 cm isometric, 1 cm square dot, 1 cm isometric dot, tracing, card

Other: Calculators, metre sticks, 180° and 360° protractors, set squares, pairs of compasses, coloured pencils, rulers, pencils, erasers, scissors, sticky tape, glue, long metric tapes, 1 cm cubes, drawing pins, trundle wheel, string

Additional equipment

Equipment	Part 1	Part 2	Part 3	Part 4
mirrors	7, W1			
9-pin nailboard and elastic bands	10, W4, 11, S11			
tiles	25			
counters (or coins)	25, S10		82	
dice	26–27	75		143–144, W3
spent matchsticks	24, W8	74	111, 112	
current calendar	30			
50p coin	34, W11			E31
½ cm and 2 cm isometric paper	32		111	
coloured paper	30, 35–36, W22			
personal weighing scales		45, W14		
stopwatch		62, W18		
dictionary		64, W30		
½ cm square dot paper	54			
Meccano strips (or card/plastic equivalents)		63, W19		
fasteners		63, W19		
acetate sheets			S37	
variety of 3D shapes			99–100, 106	
toothpaste box			104	
1 mm square paper				134, W28–29
novel				130
computer				130

(just page number) – Core Textbook
S – Support Worksheet Masters

W – Core Workbook or Worksheet Masters
E – Extension Textbook

Extra equipment for the Introductory and Additional activities

Equipment	Page
Part 1	
Bank cheques	*1*
Obtuse-angled card triangle	*8*
Set of regular polygons	*20*
Local maps	*28*
Knitting patterns	*35*
Prepared worksheet	*E7*
Part 2	
Prepared strips of paper	*S14*
Prepared worksheets	*S15/16*
Cut out card pies	*S16*
Garden centre leaflets	*49*
Map and compass	*57*
Newspaper or TV Times	*59*
Part 3	
Rubik's cube	*84*
Daily newspaper	*85*
Advertising posters to show ¼ off etc.	*90*
DIY leaflets	*S42*
Cup, litre container, measuring jug	*103*
Plasticine or clay cuboids, water or sand	*103*
Medicine bottle	*103*
Perspex or cardboard box, juice cartons	*104*
8 prepared shape cards	*107*
12 prepared letter cards	*108*
Extra copies of S36	*S36*
Part 4	
Newspaper or magazine article	*119*
Items displaying % increase or decrease	*120*
Coloured gummed paper	*125*
Envelopes, matchboxes, chalk boxes	*131*
Brochures containing house plans	*133*
Furniture catalogue	*134*
Map showing distances between towns	*E33*
Highway code	*140*
Bag and 17 marbles	*137*
Prepared OHP transparencies	*E34*
Holiday brochures	*147*
OHP and small familiar 3D objects	*S46*
Atlas	*E29*

(just page number) – Core Textbook
S – Support Worksheet Masters

W – Core Workbook or Worksheet Masters
E – Extension Textbook

MATHEMATICAL DEVELOPMENT OF HEINEMANN MATHEMATICS 8

Mathematics in the National Curriculum (England and Wales)

Part	Using and applying mathematics	Number — Knowledge and use of numbers	Number — Measures	Algebra	Shape and space	Handling data
1	Detour – half-turn symmetry (E)	Revision – place value – rounding to 10, 100 and 1000 – multiplication and division by a single-digit number and a two-digit number – multiplication and division by 10, 100 and 1000 and multiples of these Detours – flow charts – checking calculations	Decimals – notation to thousandths – multiplication and division by 2–9 – calculator work Tolerance (E) Detour – other methods	Formulae – word formulae from shape and number patterns – coordinate patterns Symbolic notation (E)	2D shape – line and rotational symmetry – classification of triangles – making shapes Tessellations	
	Extended Context: Lifescapes Exhibition Centre					
2	Strategies – guess and check – look for a pattern – mixed strategies Detour – investigating diagonals	Detours – whole numbers (S) – +, –, problem solving (S) Fractions – order, equivalence, simplification Decimals – multiplication and division by 10, 100 and 1000 and multiples of these – rounding to two decimal places Percentages – conversion to fractions – calculations based on 1% and 10% Roots by successive approximations (E)	Time – am, pm, 12- and 24-hour notation – duration – measurement in seconds	Formulae – construction and use of number machines – formulae using symbols – evaluation of formulae	Angle – measurement – 8 compass points – bearings – using compasses and protractors Detours – reflection and tiling – position fixing (S)	Bar and trend graphs – range and mean – frequency tables – discrete and continuous data – class intervals – survey sheets
3	Strategies – make a model – elimination Detours – investigating networks – investigation (S)	Number sets – multiples – factors – primes – squares – cubes Direct proportion – unitary method Fractions – multiplication by a whole number – conversion to a decimal – fraction of a whole number Additional and subtraction of fractions and mixed numbers (E) Detour – checking answers	Area – area of a triangle $A = \frac{1}{2}bc$ – composite shapes Volume – cm^3, ml, l, m^3 – volume of a cuboid as lbh – volume of a prism as Ah		3D Shape – classification – relationship between faces, vertices and edges Detours – translation and reflection (E) – shape through pattern (S)	Graphs – straight-line and curved-line Probability – bias – combined probability – tree diagrams Graphical solution of simultaneous linear equations (E)
4	Detours – matching areas investigation – colouring maps investigation (E) – number investigation (E)	Percentages – percentage increase and decrease – conversion to fractions – fractions as percentages – calculator rounding Direct calculation of percentage change (E) Detour – approximations Direct proportion – conversion graphs – construction of straight-line graphs – concept and language – calculator work	Scale – calculation of true and plan dimensions – scale drawing Speed – speed, distance, time – calculation of distance Calculation of time (E)	Equations – construction and use – inequalities and inequations Negative numbers – informal + and – – informal + and – Equations involving integers (E) Systems of inequations (E)	Angles – three-figure bearings – sum of the angles of a triangle – vertically opposite Regular polygons (E) Detours – spatial relationships (S) – constructing shapes (S)	
	Extended Context: Flight to Australia					

MATHEMATICAL DEVELOPMENT OF HEINEMANN MATHEMATICS 8

Part	Problem-Solving and Enquiry	Information Handling	Number, Money and Measurement — Whole numbers	Number, Money and Measurement — Fractions, decimals and percentages	Number, Money and Measurement — Algebra and relationships	Measure	Shape, Position and Movement
1	Detour – half-turn symmetry (E)		Revision – place value – rounding to 10, 100 and 1000 – multiplication and division by a single-digit number and a two-digit number – multiplication and division by 10, 100 and 1000 and multiples of these Detours – flowcharts – checking calculations	Decimals – notation to thousandths – multiplication and division by 2–9 – calculator work Tolerance (E) Detour – other methods	Formulae – word formulae from shape and number patterns – coordinate patterns Symbolic notation (E)	Detours – enlargement (S) – distance and direction (S)	2D Shape – line and rotational symmetry – classification of triangles – making shapes Tessellations
	Extended Context: Lifescapes Exhibition Centre						
2	Strategies – guess and check – look for a pattern – mixed strategies Detour – investigating diagonals	Bar and trend graphs – range and mean – frequency tables – discrete and continuous data – class intervals – survey sheets	Detours – whole numbers (S) – +, –, problem solving (S)	Fractions – order, equivalence, simplification Decimals – multiplication and division by 10, 100 and 1000 and multiples of these – rounding to two decimal places Percentages – conversion to fractions – calculations based on 1% and 10% Roots by successive approximations (E)	Formulae – construction and use of number machines – formulae using symbols – evaluation of formulae	Time – am, pm, 12- and 24-hour notation – duration – measurement in seconds	Angle – measurement – 8 compass points – bearings Constructions – using compasses and protractors Detours – reflection and tiling – position fixing (S)
3	Strategies – make a model – elimination Detours – investigating networks – investigation (S)	Graphs – straight-line and curved-line Probability – bias – combined probability – tree diagrams Graphical solution of simultaneous linear equations (E)	Number sets – multiples – factors – primes – squares – cubes Direct proportion – unitary method	Fractions – multiplication by a whole number – conversion to a decimal – fraction of a whole number Addition and subtraction of fractions and mixed numbers (E) Detour – checking answers		Area – area of a triangle, $A = ½bc$ – composite shapes Volume – cm^3, ml, l, m^3 – volume of a cuboid as lbh – volume of a prism as Ah	3D Shape – classification – relationship between faces, vertices and edges Detours – translation and reflection (E) – shape through pattern (S)
4	Detours – matching areas investigation – colouring maps investigation (E) – number investigation (E)	Direction proportion – conversion graphs – construction of straight-line graphs – concept and language – calculator work		Percentages – percentage increase and decrease – conversion to fractions – fractions as percentages – calculator rounding Direct calculation of percentage change (E) Detour – approximations	Equations – construction and use – inequalities and inequations Negative numbers – informal + and – Equations involving integers (E) Systems of inequations (E)	Scale – calculation of true and plan dimensions – scale drawing Speed – speed, distance, time – calculation of distance Calculation of time (E)	Angles – three-figure bearings – sum of the angles of a triangle – vertically opposite Regular polygons (E) Detours – spatial relationships (S) – constructing shapes (S)
	Extended Context: Flight to Australia						

S – Support Worksheet Masters   E – Extension Textbook

Progress Records

A number of items are offered to help teachers record the progress of their pupils.

At the end of the Core Workbook:

- A **Record of Work Grid**

In these Teacher's Notes:

- **Pupil Progress Records** linked to the National Curriculum (England and Wales) (pages T13–T16), the Mathematics 5–14 Guidelines (Scotland) (pages T17–T20) and the Common Curriculum (Northern Ireland) (pages T21–T24).
- A **Class Progress Record** (pages T25–T28).

Teachers can choose to what extent they use these materials.

Record of Work Grid

The grid at the end of the Core Workbook or photocopiable Worksheet Masters consists of a set of numbered boxes which correspond exactly to every page of the Core Textbook, Core Workbook, Support Worksheets and Extension Textbook. The grid provides a simple, convenient way of recording work attempted or completed by individual pupils. At its simplest, pupils could be instructed to tick boxes as they complete the work. However, teachers may wish to adopt a more sophisticated system, using colour codes, a variety of ticks or other symbols to indicate, for example, 'completion' or 'partial completion'.

Pupil Progress Records

A choice of Pupil Progress Records is provided showing links to the National Curriculum (England and Wales) (pages T13–T16), the Mathematics 5–14 Guidelines (Scotland) (pages T17–T20) and the Common Curriculum (Northern Ireland) (pages T21–T24). For each curriculum, four sheets are provided corresponding to Heinemann Mathematics 8 *Parts 1–4*.

The pupil's progress in each section can be summarised in the right-hand column using a code such as:

- ☐ – not attempted
- ◪ – some difficulty
- ☒ – satisfactory
- ■ – excellent

There is additional space for an overall summary of the year's work which could include general comments on progress, attitude, effort, special difficulties and so on.

It is expected that this record of progress will be maintained by the teacher and will show achievement rather than be a simple list of work attempted. Achievement will be measured in a variety of ways which are likely to include appropriate assessment items as well as teacher observation of on-going class work.

Class Progress Records

This provides an alternative method of recording the progress of a number of pupils.

Pupil progress record: *Part 1*

Name: _____

Class: _____

	England and Wales National Curriculum Statements of Attainment	S	C	E
Whole numbers 1 Place value; four operations with rounding; short methods; approximations; calculator work	UA3d/3 → 4 N2a/3; 3ab/3 → 4; 3b/4		☐	
	UA2a/4 N2a/4; 3a/4; 3bf, 4a/5			☐
2D Shape Line and rotational symmetry; classifying triangles and making shapes	UA2c/4; 2abc/5 SM2b, 3c/4; 2c/4 → 5; 2abc/5			☐
Decimals 1 Third decimal place; addition and subtraction to 2 and 3 decimal places; multiplication and division by whole numbers to 2 decimal places; calculator work Tolerance	N2b,3c/4; 2a, 3c/4 → 5 SM4b/4		☐	
	UA3d/5 N2a/4; 3c/4; 3c/4 → 5; 3ce/5 SM4a/5		☐	
	UA2ad/5 N3c, 4a/5; 3c, 4a/6; 4d/EP			☐
Tessellations Work based on Escher-like tiling	UA2c/4; 3c/5 SM2a, 3c/4; 2ab, 3c/5			☐
Word formulae Formulae in words from pattern; coordinate patterns	A2b/3 → 4; 2b/4; 3b/4 → 5	☐		
	UA2ab/5 A3b/4 → 5; 3b/5; 2b3b/5 → 6			☐
Formulae in symbols	A3ab/5 → 6			☐
Extended context 1 The Exhibition Centre	UA2c, 3d/4; 2ac, 3bd, 4ac/5 N3ce/4; 3c, 4a/5 SM3d, 4a/5; 3b,4d/5 → 6 HD2ab/4; 2f/5			☐
Detours Enlargement	SM3d/5 → 6	☐		
Distance and direction	UA3d/4 → 5	☐		
Flow charts	UA3ab/6 N3a/4			☐
Other methods	N3ab/4			☐
Checking calculator answers	N3c, 4ad/5			☐
Rotational symmetry	UA2c/6 SM3c/5			☐

Summary

© Scottish Secondary Mathematics Group 1992

Pupil progress record: *Part 2*

HEINEMANN MATHEMATICS 8

Name: _____

Class: _____

	England and Wales National Curriculum Statements of Attainment	S	C	E
Fractions 1 Concept; equivalence and simplification; addition and subtraction	N2b/4; 2b, 3c/4 → 5 HD2f/3		☐	
	N2b/5; 3c/5 → 6			☐
Handling data 1 Trend and bar-line graphs Interpretation and construction of bar graphs/ charts; mean; range; frequency tables; class intervals; survey sheets	HD2acf/4; 2cf/5		☐	
	UA4a/5 HD2c/4; 2abcde/5		☐	
	HD2f/5			☐
Decimals 2 Multiplication and division by multiples of 10, 100, 1000; approximation to whole numbers; first and second decimal place	N3c/4 → 5; 3c, 4a/5 SM4a/5; 4c/7		☐	
	UA2b/5 N2ab, 3cf, 4a/5; 4d/5 → 6			☐
Multiplication by a decimal: roots by approximation	N4b/6; 4a/7			☐
Angles 1 Naming; measuring and drawing angles; directions and bearings	UA3ad/5 SM2abdf/5		☐	
Time 12- and 24-hour notation; durations; addition and subtraction; measuring in seconds	SM4a/3; 4a/3 → 4	☐		
	SM4a/4		☐	
Percentages 1 Concept; common percentages as fractions	N2b/4; 3c/5		☐	
	N2b, 3d/5			☐
Constructions Drawing triangles and rectangles	SM2bd/5			☐
Formulae Number machines; words to symbols; evaluation	A3b/4 → 5; 3ab/5		☐	
	UA2c/5 A3ab/5			☐
Problem solving 1 Guess and check; listing; tables; pattern; mixed strategies	UA2c, 4b/5; 2abc, 3b, 4ab/5 → 6		☐	
	UA2c, 3b/5 → 6 A 2b/5			☐
Detours Whole numbers	N3a/3 → 4	☐		
Position fixing	SM3a/4	☐		
+, −, problem solving	UA2abc/4 N3a/4	☐		
Shape patterns	SM3b/4			☐
Diagonals	A2b/4 SM 2b/4			☐

T14

HEINEMANN MATHEMATICS 8

Pupil progress record: *Part 3*

Name: _____

Class: _____

	England and Wales National Curriculum Statements of Attainment	S	C	E
Whole numbers 2 Multiples; factors; primes; squares; cubes	UA2bc/5 N3a/4		☐	
Handling data 2 Straight-line; conversion and curved-line graphs	A2c/5 HD2cf/4	☐		
	A2c/5 HD2cf/5 → 6		☐	
	UA2c, 3b/5 A2c/5; 2c/6 → 7 HD2cf/5 → 6			☐
Fractions 2 Multiplication by a whole number; fraction of a whole number; vulgar to decimal fraction	N2b, 3c, 4a/6; 2b/6		☐	
Addition and subtraction	N2b, 3cd/5; 3c/5 → 6; 2b, 3c/6			☐
Area Rectangles; triangles; composite shapes; deriving formulae; for triangle, $A = \frac{1}{2}bh$	SM4d/4; 4d/5 → 6; 4d/6	☐		
	SM4d/6			☐
Proportion 1 Unitary method; comparative costs	N3c/5 → 6	☐		
	N2b, 3c, 4a/6		☐	
3D Shape Pyramids and prisms from nets; faces, vertices and edges relationship; puzzles	UA2c/5 SM2b/5; 2ab/6		☐	
Volume Reading scales; cuboids, $l \times b \times h$; prisms, cross-sectional area × height; cubic metre	UA2b/6 A3b/4 → 6 SM4ab/4; 4d/6		☐	
Probability Language; probability scale; theoretical and estimated probabilities; bias; combined events	HD2a, 3acd/5; 3e/6; 3ac/7		☐	
Problem solving 2 Make a model; elimination; mixed strategies	UA2abc/6		☐	
Detours Shape through pattern	SM2a/4 A2b/4	☐		
Investigation	UA4b/5	☐		
Networks	UA3ab/6		☐	
Approximations	N3ef, 4c/4 → 5		☐	
Translation, reflection	SM2c, 3c/5			☐

© Scottish Secondary Mathematics Group 1992

Pupil progress record: *Part 4*

Name: _____

Class: _____

England and Wales
National Curriculum
Statements of Attainment

	S	C	E

Percentages 2
Decrease and increase; fractions as percentages; calculator rounding

Statements	S	C	E
N2b, 3c/5; 2b, 3cd/6 HD2f/5		☐	
N2b, 3df/6 HD 2ab/5			☐

Angles 2
Bearings; port; starboard; angle sum; angles in a triangle
Regular polygons

Statements	S	C	E
SM2d/5 → 6; 2d/6			☐
SM2bd/5; 2bc, 3d/6			☐

Proportion 2
Unitary method using a calculator; straight-line graphs

Statements	S	C	E
N3c, 4a/5		☐	
N3c, 4a/5 SM4a/5 HD2f/5			☐

Length and scale
The millimetre; scale calculations and scale drawing

Statements	S	C	E
SM3d, 4a/5		☐	
UA2c/6 N2b, 3c/6 SM3d, 4ab/5; 3d/6			☐

Speed
Speed, distance and time

Statements	S	C	E
SM4c/7			☐
SM4c/7			☐

Equations
$x + a = b$; $x - a = b$; $ax - b$; inequalities and inequations

Double inequalities

Statements	S	C	E
A2a, 3acd/6; 3acd/6 → 7			☐
A3acd/6; 3acd/6 → 7			☐

Negative numbers
Ordering; informal addition and subtraction; coordinate work

Equations

Statements	S	C	E
N2b, 3c/5 SM 3a/5			☐
N3c/5 A3bcd/6 SM3a/5			☐

Extended context 2
Flight to Australia

Statements	S	C	E
UA3ad/5; 2ac, 3bde/6 N3b/5 A 2c, 3b/6 SM2d, 3d, 4a/5; 2a/6; 4c/7			☐

Detours
Spatial relationships

Constructing shapes

Approximation

Area problem

Regions in rectangles

Mystic cube

Statements	S	C	E
SM2a/4 → 5		☐	
UA2abd/4		☐	
N3f/6 → 7			☐
UA2ab, 4a/6 SM4d/6			☐
UA2cd, 4b/6			☐
UA2abd, 3bd/6			☐

T16

Name: _____

Class: _____

Scotland
Mathematics 5–14
Attainment targets

	S	C	E

Whole numbers 1
Place value; four operations with rounding; short methods; approximations; calculator work

Target	S	C	E
C/D; RTN/D; AS/D; MD/D; RN/D		☐	
PSE; RTN/D; AS/D; MD/D, E; RN/D			☐

2D Shape
Line and rotational symmetry; classifying triangles and making shapes

Target	S	C	E
PSE; I/E; RS/D, E; PM/D; S/D, E; A/C		☐	

Decimals 1
Third decimal place; addition and subtraction to 2 and 3 decimal places; multiplication and division by whole numbers to 2 decimal places; calculator work

Target	S	C	E
RTN/D; AS/D; ME/C		☐	
PSE; O/D; I/D; RTN/D, E; AS/E; MD/D, E; ME/D		☐	

Tolerance

Target	S	C	E
PSE; I/E; RTN/E; AS/D, E; MD/E; E+			☐

Tessellations
Work based on Escher-like tiling

Target	S	C	E
PSE; RS/D; PM/D; S/E		☐	

Word formulae
Formulae in words from pattern; coordinate patterns

Target	S	C	E
FE/D		☐	
PSE; PS/E; FE/D, E; S/E			☐

Formulae in symbols

Target	S	C	E
PS/E; FE/E; E+			☐

Extended context 1
The Exhibition Centre

Target	S	C	E
PSE; C/D; D/C; I/E; MD/C, D; ME/E; T/C; PFS/E; PM/C; S/E			☐

Detours

Enlargement

Target	S	C	E
RS/C		☐	

Distance and direction

Target	S	C	E
PM/C		☐	

Flow charts

Target	S	C	E
PSE; I/E; AS/C; MD/C			☐

Other methods

Target	S	C	E
AS/D; MD/D			☐

Checking calculator answers

Target	S	C	E
I/E; AS/D; MD/E			☐

Rotational symmetry

Target	S	C	E
PSE; PM/D; S/E			☐

Summary

Pupil progress record: *Part 2*

Name: _____

Class: _____

	Scotland Mathematics 5–14 Attainment targets	S	C	E
---	---	:-::	:-:	:-:
Fractions 1 Concept; equivalence and simplification; addition and subtraction	I/C; RTN/D; FPR/C	☐		
	RTN/E		☐	
Handling data 1 Trend and bar-line graphs Interpretation and construction of bar graphs/ charts; mean; range; frequency tables; class intervals; survey sheets	PSE; C/D; O/D; D/D; I/D	☐		
	PSE; C/D, E; O/E; D/D; I/D, E; E+		☐	
	O/E; I/E			☐
Decimals 2 Multiplication and division by multiples of 10, 100, 1000; approximation to whole numbers; first and second decimal place Multiplication by a decimal: roots by approximation	PSE; RTN/D; MD/D; RN/D; ME/D	☐		
	RTN/E; MD/D, E; RN/D, E; PS/E; ME/E; E+		☐	
	PSE; RTN/E; MD/E; FE/E; PFS/E			☐
Angles 1 Naming; measuring and drawing angles; directions and bearings	PSE; RS/D; PM/D, E; A/D, E	☐		
Time 12- and 24-hour notation; durations; addition and subtraction; measuring in seconds	PSE; T/C, D	☐		
	PSE; RTN/D, AS/E; T/D, E		☐	
Percentages 1 Concept; common percentages as fractions	RTN/D; FPR/D	☐		
	D/E; RTN/D; FPR/E		☐	
Constructions Drawing triangles and rectangles	PSE; PFS/E; RS/E; A/E	☐		
Formulae Number machines; words to symbols; evaluation	FE/E	☐		
	PSE; I/E; FE/E; PFS/D			☐
Problem solving 1 Guess and check; listing; tables; pattern; mixed strategies	PSE; O/D; AS/D; MD/D; PS/E; FE/D, E; ME/D; PFS/E	☐		
	PSE; O/D; FE/E			☐
Detours Whole numbers	AS/D; MD/C	☐		
Position fixing	PM/B	☐		
+, −, problem solving	PSE; AS/D	☐		
Shape patterns	PSE; S/D, E			☐
Diagonals	PSE; FE/D; RS/D			☐

Pupil progress record: *Part 3*

HEINEMANN MATHEMATICS 8

Name: _____

Class: _____

Scotland
Mathematics 5–14
Attainment targets

	S	C	E

Whole numbers 2
Multiples; factors; primes; squares; cubes

PSE; MD/D; PS/E; FE/D; PM/D		☐	

Handling data 2
Straight-line; conversion and curved-line graphs

D/D; I/C		☐	
D/D, E; I/D, E; M/E; ME/D		☐	
D/D, E; I/D, E; FE/D; ME/D			☐

Fractions 2
Multiplication by a whole number; fraction of a whole number; vulgar to decimal fraction
Addition and subtraction

RTN/D, E; FPR/D, E; E+		☐	
D/E; RTN/E; FPR/E; ME/D; E+			☐

Area
Rectangles; triangles; composite shapes; deriving formulae; for triangle, $A = \frac{1}{2}bh$

FE/D; ME/C, D, E; PFS/E; E+		☐	
PFS/E; E+			☐

Proportion 1
Unitary method; comparative costs

RTN/C; MD/C, D; FPR/E		☐	
PSE; MD/D, E; FPR/E			☐

3D Shape
Pyramids and prisms from nets; faces, vertices and edges relationship; puzzles

PSE; FE/D; RS/C, D, E		☐	

Volume
Reading scales; cuboids, $l \times b \times h$; prisms, cross-sectional area × height; cubic metre

PSE; FE/D; ME/C, D, E; PFS/E; RS/C, D		☐	

Probability
Language; probability scale; theoretical and estimated probabilities; bias; combined events

C/C; O/C, D, E; D/C; I/C; E+; RS/D, E		☐	

Problem solving 2
Make a model; elimination; mixed strategies

PSE; AS/D; PS/D, E		☐	

Detours
Shape through pattern

S/D	☐		

Investigation

PSE	☐		

Networks

PSE; FE/E		☐	

Approximations

I/E; AS/D; MD/D; RN/D		☐	

Translation, reflection

PM/D; S/D, E			☐

Pupil progress record: *Part 4*

Name: _____

Class: _____

	Scotland Mathematics 5–14 Attainment targets	S	C	E
---	---	:---::	:---:	:---:
Percentages 2 Decrease and increase; fractions as percentages; calculator rounding	PSE; C/E; D/D, E; I/D, E; RTN/D; AS/D; RN/D; FPR/E		☐	
	PSE; C/E; D/D, E; I/D; RTN/D; RN/D; FPR/E			☐
Angles 2 Bearings; port; starboard; angle sum; angles in a triangle Regular polygons	PSE; PM/D; A/D, E		☐	
	PSE; RS/D; S/D, E; A/E; E+			☐
Proportion 2 Unitary method using a calculator; straight-line graphs	MD/D	☐		
	PSE; D/E; I/D; MD/D, E; RN/D; ME/D	☐		
Length and scale The millimetre; scale calculations and scale drawing	RTN/D; ME/D	☐		
	RTN/D; FPR/E; ME/D; PFS/E		☐	
Speed Speed, distance and time	MD/D, E; RN/D; T/D; E+		☐	
	MD/D, E; ME/D; T/D; PFS/E; E+			☐
Equations $x + a = b$; $x - a = b$; $ax = b$; inequalities and inequations Double inequalities	RTN/D; FE/E; E+		☐	
	PSE; FE/E; ME/D; E+			☐
Negative numbers Ordering; informal addition and subtraction; coordinate work Equations	PSE; RTN/E; AS/E; FE/E; RS/E; PM/E		☐	
	PSE; RTN/E; AS/E; FE/E; PM/E; S/E			☐
Extended context 2 Flight to Australia	PSE; D/E; I/E; M/E; AS/D; MD/D; FPR/D; PS/D, E; FE/D; ME/D; T/D; PFS/E; RS/D; PM/D, E; A/D, E		☐	
Detours Spatial relationships	PSE; RS/C, D	☐		
Constructing shapes	PSE; RS/D	☐		
Approximation	RTN/D; AS/D; MD/D, E; RN/D; PM/D		☐	
Area problem	PSE; I/E; PFS/E		☐	
Regions in rectangles	PSE; PS/D; FE/D			☐
Mystic cube	PSE; AS/D; RS/D			☐

Pupil progress record: *Part 1*

Name: _____

Class: _____

	Northern Ireland Common Curriculum Statements of Attainment	S	C	E
Whole numbers 1 Place value; four operations with rounding; short methods; approximations; calculator work	N4abcgijl	☐		
	P4b N3e; N4abcgijl; N5fgk; N6ef; N7h		☐	
2D Shape Line and rotational symmetry; classifying triangles and making shapes	P4ad A4f S4abd; S5abcd; S6ade		☐	
Decimals 1 Third decimal place; addition and subtraction to 2 and 3 decimal places; multiplication and division by whole numbers to 2 decimal places; calculator work	N4dkl; N6a	☐		
	P4b; P5b; P6ab N3g; N4kl; N5f; N6a M4a; M5c		☐	
Tolerance	P4b; P6ab N4k; N6ab			☐
Tessellations Work based on Escher-like tiling	S5a; S6a		☐	
Word formulae Fomulae in words from pattern; coordinate patterns	A3a; A4b; A5b	☐		
	A4bdf; A5b; A6a S4d		☐	
Formulae in symbols	P5ab A4bd; A5bd; A6c			☐
Extended context 1 The Exhibition Centre	P4abd; P5abf; P6ab N3eg; N4hj; N5h M4d; M5a; M6a S4d; S6f D5ae		☐	
Detours Enlargement	S6f	☐		
Distance and direction	P5b	☐		
Flow charts	P4b; P5b N4ghi			☐
Other methods	N4ghi			☐
Checking calculator answers	N3e; N4jkl A4e			☐
Rotational symmetry	P5ab S5cd			☐

Pupil progress record: *Part 2*

Name: _____

Class: _____

	Northern Ireland Common Curriculum Statements of Attainment	S	C	E
Fractions 1 Concept; equivalence and simplification; addition and subtraction	N3c; N5bh D3c	☐		
	N3c; N5b		☐	
Handling data 1 Trend and bar-line graphs	P3abc D3ac; D4aef	☐		
Interpretation and construction of bar graphs/charts; mean; range; frequency tables; class intervals; survey sheets	P5abe D4ab; D5abd; D6bh		☐	
	P5b D3c; D4ef			☐
Decimals 2 Multiplication and division by multiples of 10, 100, 1000; approximation to whole numbers; first and second decimal place	P5b N3egi; N4dgiln M5b D4b	☐		
	N4dkln; N5fl; N6a M5c D4b		☐	
Multiplication by a decimal; roots by approximation	P4b; P5b; P6ab; P7b N4d; N5kl; N7d M6c			☐
Angles 1 Naming; measuring and drawing angles; directions and bearings	P5b M4d; M5ad S4a; S7b		☐	
Time 12- and 24-hour notation; durations; addition and subtraction; measuring in seconds	P5b M3b; M4a	☐		
	P5b N3g; N4dk M4a		☐	
Percentages 1 Concept; common percentages as fractions	P5b N3e; N4fh; N5ch; N6b	☐		
	N4f; N5ch; N6b D6e		☐	
Constructions Drawing triangles and rectangles	P5abef M5ad; M6a S4b		☐	
Formulae Number machines; words to symbols; evaluation	N4gi A3d; A5de; A6bc		☐	
	P5bcd A5de M4b D6g			☐
Problem solving 1 Guess and check; listing; tables; pattern; mixed strategies	P4a; b; P5bcde N4hij; N5afk A4ab; A5b M4c; M5e		☐	
	P5be; P6d; P7d A4d; A5b; A6a			☐
Detours Whole numbers	N4ghi A3a	☐		
Position fixing	S4d	☐		
+, −, problem solving	P5b N4h	☐		
Shape patterns	P4d S6e		☐	
Diagonals	P5abe A4b; A5b S4b		☐	

Pupil progress record: *Part 3*

Name: _____

Class: _____

	Northern Ireland Common Curriculum Statements of Attainment	S	C	E
Whole numbers 2 Multiples; factors; primes; squares; cubes	P4ad; P5acd N4g; N5a A4abcf; A5abc		☐	
Handling data 2 Straight-line; conversion and curved-line graphs	D3a; D4f		☐	
	M5b; M6d D4f; D5f		☐	
	N6e A6g; A7f M5b D4ef			☐
Fractions 2 Multiplication by a whole number; fraction of a whole number; vulgar to decimal fraction Addition and subtraction	P5cd N3c; N5bhj; N6b; N7f		☐	
	P4d N5bl; N6b; N7f M5c D4f; D5f			☐
Area Rectangles; triangles; composite shapes; deriving formulae; for triangle, $A = \frac{1}{2}bh$	A4d M3c; M4c	☐		
	A4bd; A5e M5e		☐	
Proportion 1 Unitary method; comparative costs	N3g; N4gil; N5j M4a	☐		
	N3eg; N4gil; N6e		☐	
3D Shape Pyramids and prisms from nets; faces; vertices and edges relationship; puzzles	P4d; P5cd A5e S4b; S5a; S6b		☐	
Volume Reading scales; cuboids, $l \times b \times h$; prisms, cross-sectional area × height; cubic metre	P5abf A4d; A5e M4acd; M5ce; M6c S4b; S6b		☐	
Probability Language; probability scale; theoretical and estimated probabilities; bias; combined events	P4c; P5ab S4b D3f; D4hi; D5agh; D6ij		☐	
Problem solving 2 Make a model; elimination; mixed strategies	P4d; P5abef N3g; N6a A5b M5a; M6a		☐	
Detours Shape through pattern	P4d; P5b	☐		
Investigation	P4d; P5b	☐		
Networks	P4d; P5abe		☐	
Approximations, checking answers	N4jmo; N7h A4e		☐	
Translation, reflection	P4d; P5bf S6e			☐

Pupil progress record: *Part 4*

Name: _____

Class: _____

	Northern Ireland Common Curriculum Statements of Attainment	S	C	E
Percentages 2 Decrease and increase; fractions as percentages; calculator rounding	P5ab N4fn; N5bhl; N6bc; N7f D5ae; D6e		☐	
	P5ab N5bhjl; N6bc; N7f D3c; D5a			☐
Angles 2 Bearings; port; starboard; angle sum; angles in a triangle	P5bcd M5d S4a; S5ab; S7b		☐	
Regular polygons	P5ab M5d S5acd; S6a			☐
Proportion 2 Unitary method using a calculator; straight-line graphs	N4l	☐		
	P4bP5b; P6b N4jl M5bc D4f; D5f		☐	
Length and scale The millimetre; scale calculations and scale drawing	M3ab; M4a; M5c	☐		
	N5d M4a; M5ac; M6ac		☐	
Speed Speed, distance and time	P5b N4in; N5f M4a; M6b		☐	
	N4i; N5f M4a; M5a; M6b			☐
Equations $x + a = b$; $x - a = b$; $ax - b$; inequalities and inequations	N6a M4b A5e; A6d		☐	
Double inequalities	P5ab A7d M6b			☐
Negative numbers Ordering; informal addition and subtraction; coordinate work	P5a, b N5i A5f S4b; S5e		☐	
Equations	N5i A5ef; A6d S5e			☐
Extended context 2 Flight to Australia	P4d; P5abcdef N3e; N4ijk; N5h A4b; A5bce; A6a M5acd; M6abd S6b; S7b D4f		☐	
Detours Spatial relationships	P5bf S6b	☐		
Constructing shapes	P4d S4b	☐		
Approximation	N4g; N6gf; N7h A4f			☐
Area problem	P4bd; P5abf; P6ab M5ac; M6a			☐
Regions in rectangles	P4bd; P5bcdf; P6ab A4b			☐
Mystic cube	P5b N4i S4b; S6b			☐

© Scottish Secondary Mathematics Group 1993

Class progress record: *Part 1*

S ☐
C ☐
E ☐ ↓

Class: _____

Detours

Pupil	Whole numbers 1	2D Shape	Decimals 1	Tessellations	Word formulae	Extended context 1	Flow charts	Other methods	Checking calculator answers	Enlargement	Distance and direction	Rotational symmetry			Comments

Class progress record: *Part 2*

HEINEMANN 8
MATHEMATICS

S ☐
C ☐
E ☐ ↓

Detours

Class: _____

Pupil

Column headers (diagonal):
Fractions 1, Handling data 1, Decimals 2, Angles 1, Time, Percentages 1, Constructions, Formulae, Problem solving 1, Shape patterns, Diagonals, Whole numbers, Position fixing, +, −, ÷ problem solving

Comments

© Scottish Secondary Mathematics Group 1992

T26

Detours

S ☐
C ☐
E ☐ ↓

Class: _____

Pupil	Whole numbers 2	Handling data 2	Fractions 2	Area	Proportion 1	3D Shape	Volume	Probability	Problem solving 2	Networks	Approximations	Shape through pattern	Investigation	Translation/reflection		Comments
	☐	☐☐	☐☐	☐	☐	☐	☐	☐	☐	☐	☐	☐	☐		
	☐	☐☐	☐☐	☐	☐	☐	☐	☐	☐	☐	☐	☐	☐		
	☐	☐☐	☐☐	☐	☐	☐	☐	☐	☐	☐	☐	☐	☐		
	☐	☐☐	☐☐	☐	☐	☐	☐	☐	☐	☐	☐	☐	☐		
	☐	☐☐	☐☐	☐	☐	☐	☐	☐	☐	☐	☐	☐	☐		
	☐	☐☐	☐☐	☐	☐	☐	☐	☐	☐	☐	☐	☐	☐		
	☐	☐☐	☐☐	☐	☐	☐	☐	☐	☐	☐	☐	☐	☐		
	☐	☐☐	☐☐	☐	☐	☐	☐	☐	☐	☐	☐	☐	☐		
	☐	☐☐	☐☐	☐	☐	☐	☐	☐	☐	☐	☐	☐	☐		
	☐	☐☐	☐☐	☐	☐	☐	☐	☐	☐	☐	☐	☐	☐		
	☐	☐☐	☐☐	☐	☐	☐	☐	☐	☐	☐	☐	☐	☐		
	☐	☐☐	☐☐	☐	☐	☐	☐	☐	☐	☐	☐	☐	☐		
	☐	☐☐	☐☐	☐	☐	☐	☐	☐	☐	☐	☐	☐	☐		
	☐	☐☐	☐☐	☐	☐	☐	☐	☐	☐	☐	☐	☐	☐		
	☐	☐☐	☐☐	☐	☐	☐	☐	☐	☐	☐	☐	☐	☐		

HEINEMANN MATHEMATICS 8

Detours

S ☐
C ☐
E ☐ ↓

Class: _____

Pupil	Percentages 2	Angles 2	Proportion 2	Length and Scale	Speed	Equations	Negative numbers	Extended context 2	Approximation	Area problem	Spatial relationships	Constructing shapes	Regions in rectangles	Mystic cube		Comments
	☐☐	☐☐	☐☐	☐☐	☐☐	☐☐	☐☐	☐	☐	☐	☐☐	☐☐	☐☐			
	☐☐	☐☐	☐☐	☐☐	☐☐	☐☐	☐☐	☐	☐	☐	☐☐	☐☐	☐☐			
	☐☐	☐☐	☐☐	☐☐	☐☐	☐☐	☐☐	☐	☐	☐	☐☐	☐☐	☐☐			
	☐☐	☐☐	☐☐	☐☐	☐☐	☐☐	☐☐	☐	☐	☐	☐☐	☐☐	☐☐			
	☐☐	☐☐	☐☐	☐☐	☐☐	☐☐	☐☐	☐	☐	☐	☐☐	☐☐	☐☐			
	☐☐	☐☐	☐☐	☐☐	☐☐	☐☐	☐☐	☐	☐	☐	☐☐	☐☐	☐☐			
	☐☐	☐☐	☐☐	☐☐	☐☐	☐☐	☐☐	☐	☐	☐	☐☐	☐☐	☐☐			
	☐☐	☐☐	☐☐	☐☐	☐☐	☐☐	☐☐	☐	☐	☐	☐☐	☐☐	☐☐			
	☐☐	☐☐	☐☐	☐☐	☐☐	☐☐	☐☐	☐	☐	☐	☐☐	☐☐	☐☐			
	☐☐	☐☐	☐☐	☐☐	☐☐	☐☐	☐☐	☐	☐	☐	☐☐	☐☐	☐☐			
	☐☐	☐☐	☐☐	☐☐	☐☐	☐☐	☐☐	☐	☐	☐	☐☐	☐☐	☐☐			
	☐☐	☐☐	☐☐	☐☐	☐☐	☐☐	☐☐	☐	☐	☐	☐☐	☐☐	☐☐			
	☐☐	☐☐	☐☐	☐☐	☐☐	☐☐	☐☐	☐	☐	☐	☐☐	☐☐	☐☐			
	☐☐	☐☐	☐☐	☐☐	☐☐	☐☐	☐☐	☐	☐	☐	☐☐	☐☐	☐☐			
	☐☐	☐☐	☐☐	☐☐	☐☐	☐☐	☐☐	☐	☐	☐	☐☐	☐☐	☐☐			

HEINEMANN MATHEMATICS 8
REVISED NATIONAL CURRICULUM SUMMARY CHART

	Programme of Study												
	Using and Applying			Number			Algebra		Shape, Space and Measures			Handling Data	
	2	3	4	2	3	4	2	3	2	3	4	2	3
Whole Numbers 1	a	d		a	abf	a							
2D shape	abc								abc	c			
Decimals 1	ad	d		ab	ce	ad					ab		
Tessellations	c	c							ab	c			
Word formulae	ab						b	ab					
Extended context 1	ac	bd	ac		ce	a				bd	ad	abf	
Detours	c	abd			abc	ad				cd			
Fractions 1				b	c							f	
Handling data 1			a									abcdef	
Decimals 2	b			ab	cf	abd					ac		
Angles 1		ad							abdf				
Time											a		
Percentages 1				b	cd								
Constructions									bd				
Formulae	c							ab					
Problem solving 1	abc	b	ab				b						
Detours	abc				a		b		b	ab			
Whole numbers 2	bc				a								
Handling data 2	c	b					c					cf	
Fractions 2				b	cd	a							
Area											d		
Proportion 1				b	c	a							
3D shape	c						ab						
Volume	b							b			abd		
Probablity												a	acde
Problem solving 2	abc												
Detours		ab	b		ef	c	b		ac	c			
Percentages 2				b	cdf							abf	
Angles 2									bcd	d			
Proportion 2					c	a					a	f	
Length and scale	c			b	c					d	ab		
Speed											c		
Equations							a	acd					
Negative numbers				b	c			bcd		a			
Extended context 2	ac	abde				b	c	b	ad	d	ac		
Detours	abcd	bd	ab			f	a				d		
Summary	abcd	abcde	abc	ab	abcdef	abcd	abc	abcd	abcdf	abcd	abcd	abcdef	acde

HEINEMANN MATHEMATICS 8   MATHEMATICS 5–14 SUMMARY CHART

Information Handling

Number, Money & Measurement

Shape, Position & Movement

Level E

Level D

PSE

C, O, D, I, RTN, M, AS, MD, RN, FPR, PS, FE, ME, T, PFS, RS, PM, S, A

Whole numbers 1
2D Shape
Decimals 1
Tessellations
Word formulae
Extended context 1
Detours

Fractions 1
Handling data 1
Decimals 2
Angles 1
Time
Percentages 1
Constructions
Formulae
Problem solving 1
Detours

Whole numbers 2
Handling data 2
Fractions 2
Area
Proportion 1
3D Shape
Volume
Probability
Problem solving 2
Detours

Percentages 2
Angles 2
Proportion 2
Length and scale
Speed
Equations
Negative numbers
Extended context 2
Detours

Summary

HEINEMANN MATHEMATICS 8   COMMON CURRICULUM SUMMARY CHART

	Processes in Mathematics			Number			Algebra			Measures			Shape and Space			Handling Data		
	4	5	6	4	5	6	4	5	6	4	5	6	4	5	6	4	5	6
Whole numbers 1																		
2D Shape																		
Decimals 1																		
Tessellations																		
Word formulae																		
Extended context 1																		
Detours																		
Fractions 1																		
Handling data 1																		
Decimals 2																		
Angles 1																		
Time																		
Percentages 1																		
Constructions																		
Formulae																		
Problem solving 1																		
Detours																		
Whole numbers 2																		
Handling data 2																		
Fractions 2																		
Area																		
Proportion 1																		
3D Shape																		
Volume																		
Probability																		
Problem solving 2																		
Detours																		
Percentages 2																		
Angles 2																		
Proportion 2																		
Length and scale																		
Speed																		
Equations																		
Negative numbers																		
Extended context 2																		
Detours																		
Summary																		

HEINEMANN MATHEMATICS 8

Teaching Notes

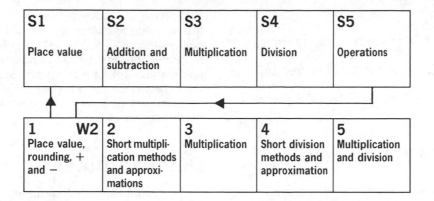

S1	S2	S3	S4	S5
Place value	Addition and subtraction	Multiplication	Division	Operations

1 W2	2	3	4	5
Place value, rounding, + and −	Short multiplication methods and approximations	Multiplication	Short division methods and approximation	Multiplication and division

CONTENT AND DEVELOPMENT

Core

The whole number work in Heinemann Mathematics 7 consists of approximation to the nearest 10, 100, 1000, addition and subtraction and 'short' and 'long' multiplication and division.

Heinemann Mathematics 8, *Whole Numbers 1*, covers:

- place value
- rounding to the nearest 10, 100, 1000
- addition and subtraction of up to four-digit numbers
- long and short multiplication and division of two- and three-digit numbers
- multiplication and division by 10, 100, 1000 and multiples of these
- estimation based on informal rounding to one significant figure; multiplication and division of two- and three-digit numbers by a two-digit number.

Whole Numbers 2, in Part 3, deals with sets of numbers including primes, squares, cubes and others.

Support

S1–S5 provide 'parallel' work to that of the Core.

National Curriculum (England and Wales)

UA2a, 3d
N2a, 3abf, 4a

Mathematics 5–14 (Scotland)

RTN/D1, 2
RN/D1
AS/D2, 3
MD/D1, 2, 3, 4   MD/E1, 2, 3, 4
PSE
E+

RELATED ACTIVITIES

Whole numbers in the environment
You could ask pupils to bring in examples of the use of whole numbers that they come across in everyday life, for example, newspaper cuttings or labels like the following:

Balance of payments £3 billion in the red?

Glasgow Rangers   0 Bathgate Thistle   12

Fiesta – For Sale £3650

Baked Beans 300g

These may be categorised as numbers which are rounded, estimated, exact, give measurements and so on.

EQUIPMENT

Calculator.

For an Introductory activity: samples of bank cheques and other related banking materials; prepared OHP transparency.

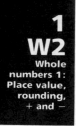

1
W2
Whole
numbers 1:
Place value,
rounding,
+ and −

N2a/4

RTN/D1
RN/D1
AS/D2

Content

- Place value to thousands including writing numbers in words
- Rounding to the nearest ten, hundred and thousand
- Addition and subtraction of up to four-digit numbers.

Introductory activities

1 Writing cheques
Prepare an OHP transparency showing cheques. Use these with overlays to revise the writing of amounts in both words and figures. If possible, produce 'chequebooks' for the pupils to complete. The discussion should cover appropriate banking language such as 'deposit', 'withdrawal' and 'teller'. Some banks will supply teaching material and this could also be used to stimulate interest.

2 Revision of rounding
If buying the following items
personal stereo £134   computer £289
rounding could be used to obtain quickly an approximate total for the purchases. Approximate total costs could also be found for items in the thousands of pounds before discussing non-monetary figures.

Detailed notes

Q3, table Emphasise that an amount which is exactly midway between two values, can be rounded either up or down.

Equipment

For Introductory activity 1:
samples of bank cheques and other related banking materials, prepared OHP transparency.

2
Whole
numbers 1:
Short
multiplication
methods and
approximations

N3a/4;
3f/5

MD/D1, 2, 3
MD/E1, 2
RN/D1

Content

- Multiplication of of two- and three-digit numbers by a single-digit number
- Mental multiplication by 10, 100, 1000 and multiples of these
- Estimation based on informal rounding to one significant figure; multiplication of two- and three-digit numbers by a two-digit number.

Introductory activity

Multiplication by 10, 100, 1000 and multiples of these
Diagrams like the following could be used to illustrate the processes involved.

Tth	Th	H	T	U	
			1	8	
		1	8	0	← 18 × 10
	1	8	0	0	← 18 × 100
1	8	0	0	0	← 18 × 1000

or

Tth	Th	H	T	U	
			2	1	
			6	3	← 21 × 3
6	3	0	0	0	← 63 × 1000
2	1	0	0	0	← 21 × 1000
6	3	0	0	0	← 21 000 × 3

Detailed notes

Q1 The range of multiplication language may need to be discussed.

Panel above Q3 It is difficult to calculate 24 × 36 mentally. An approximate product can be found using rounding. This technique is useful when an approximate value will suffice and for checking the validity of calculations.

Q8 Advise the pupils to give their answers in pounds.

Equipment

None.

Content

- Multiplication of two-, three- and four-digit numbers by a two-digit number.

The balance between paper and pencil work and use of a calculator should be determined by the teacher.

Introductory activity

Car costs
Class discussion could include the advantages/disadvantages of diesel fuel, 'trading-in', and expenses claims.

Detailed notes

Panel above Q6	An additional point to highlight here is the calculation required (2030 − 1200) to obtain the 830.
Q6	Each expense involves a fixed amount of £216 for the first 1200 km travelled.
Q7	The phrase '10p per kilometre after that' may cause difficulty.

Equipment

Calculator.

Content

- Division of two-, three- and four-digit numbers by a single-digit number
- Mental division by 10, 100, 1000 and multiples of these
- Estimation based on informal rounding to one significant figure – division of three-digit numbers by a two-digit number.

Introductory activity

Division by 10, 100, 1000 and multiples of these
Diagrams like the following could be used to illustrate the processes involved.

	Tth	Th	H	T	U
	7	2	0	0	0
72 000 ÷ 10 →		7	2	0	0
72 000 ÷ 100 →			7	2	0
72 000 ÷ 1000 →				7	2

or

	Tth	Th	H	T	U
	2	4	0	0	0
24 000 ÷ 3 →		8	0	0	0
8 000 ÷ 1000 →					8
24 000 ÷ 1000 →				2	4
24 ÷ 3 →					8

Detailed notes

| Q6 | Pupils should first convert pounds to pence. |

Equipment

None.

Content

- Estimation based on informal rounding to one significant figure
- Multiplication of a two-digit number by a two-digit number
- Division of a four-digit number (money in decimal form) by a two-digit number.

The *Challenge* provided in Q11 requires the use of problem solving strategies.

Detailed notes

| Q1,2 | These questions should be attempted without a calculator, using rounding. |
| Challenge Q11 | Give pupils the following hint if they have difficulty in finding an appropriate strategy. |

Make and extend this table:

Number of tins of		Profit
cream rice	bean stew	
1	9	
2	8	
3		

Equipment

Calculator

5
Whole numbers 1: Multiplication and division

UA2a/4
N3b, 4a/5

RN/D1
MD/D4
MD/E1, 2, 3, 4
PSE

S1
Whole numbers 1: Place value

N2a/3

RTN/D1, 2
RN/D1

Content

- Whole numbers to millions, including writing numbers in words and figures
- Rounding to the nearest 100, 1000.

Introductory activity

The sports centre
The work could be introduced by discussing a local sports facility, for example, a swimming pool or a sports centre.

Discussion could include the following:
- number of seats for spectators
- dimensions of the pool, hall, and so on
- volume of water in the pool.

The discussion should focus on which information is approximate and which is exact. Discuss the difference between exact numbers and numbers appropriately rounded. It may be useful to record the numbers both in words and in figures.

Detailed notes

| Number lines above Q7 and Q9 | These are provided to assist pupils with the rounding. |

| Q8 | The numbers in the table for Saturday and Sunday may cause difficulty because they are harder to locate on the number line. |

Equipment
None.

S2
Whole numbers 1: Addition and subtraction

N2a/3

RTN/D1
AS/D2

Content

- Addition and subtraction of three-digit numbers
- Ordering numbers.

The method for written subtraction previously used is described on page I2 of these notes.

Introductory activity

The school house system
A discussion about school house systems and competitive activities that may take place might be useful to set the scene.

Equipment
None.

S3
Whole numbers 1: Multiplication

N3ab/
3 → 4

MD/D1, 2, 3

Content

- Completion of a 10 × 10 multiplication table
- Multiplication of one- and two-digit numbers by a single-digit number
- Mental multiplication by 10, 100.

Introductory activity

Multiplication by 10, 100
A suggested approach to the revision of these processes is given in the Introductory activity for Core Textbook page 2.

Detailed notes

| Q1 | Some pupils may complete the table by repeated addition. |

Additional activity

Patterns
You could ask pupils to investigate number patterns in the 10 × 10 table in Q1.

Equipment
None.

Content

- Division of two- and three-digit numbers by a single-digit number
- Mental division of up to five-digit whole numbers by 10, 100.

Introductory activity

Division by 10, 100
A suggested approach is given in the Introductory activity for Core Textbook page 4.

Detailed notes

Q3 Some explanation may be needed about how to complete the targets.

Q4b Some explanation may be needed about how the code works.
The 14 boxes which make up the message at the foot of the page are completed by writing the appropriate code letter which corresponds to the correct answer to the questions in Q4a.

Equipment

None.

Content

- The four operations using a calculator.

Introductory activity

Calculator words
It may be worthwhile discussing how to make calculator words like those on the second half of the page. The following examples cover each of the four operations:

NOT LOW	3065 + 1549	(4614 HIGH)
OPPOSITE OF WIN	6420 − 2913	(3507 LOSE)
MARSHY GROUND	16 × 38	(608 BOG)
USED FOR WALKING	8918 ÷ 14	(637 LEG)

Some pupils may have difficulty in recognising some of the letters made from the digits, particularly the digit 6 which represents a lower case g. This list may be useful for making up additional words.

0	1	2	3	4	5	6	7	8	9
O	I	Z	E	h	S	g	L	B	none

Detailed notes

Cross-number square Pupils may need to be reminded of how to fill in a crossnumber puzzle using down and across clues. They should be aware of the 'self-correcting' nature of the puzzle.

Equipment

Calculator.

2D SHAPE

7 W1	8	9 W4	10 W4	11 W20 W21
Line and rotational symmetry	Rotation	Classification of triangles by sides	Classification of triangles by angles	Construction of shapes

CONTENT AND DEVELOPMENT

Core

Heinemann Mathematics 7 contains work on line and rotational symmetry and on isosceles, equilateral and right-angled triangles.

In Heinemann Mathematics 8 this work is revised, consolidated and developed to include:

- properties of scalene, acute-angled and obtuse-angled triangles
- classification of triangles by sides and by angles
- construction of equilateral triangles
- the use of pairs of triangles to form quadrilaterals.

National Curriculum (England and Wales)

UA2abc
SM2abc, 3c

Mathematics 5–14 (Scotland)

I/E1
RS/D2, 3   RS/E2, 5
S/D1, 2   S/E1, 2
PM/D3, 4
A/C2
PSE

RELATED ACTIVITIES

Line and rotational symmetry display
Car badges, logos, symbols and designs from advertising showing line and rotational symmetry should be collected and displayed.

Pupils could make symmetry 'pictures' on squared paper, on isometric paper, or with an ink blot on folded paper.

There is potential for cross-curricular work in art.

EQUIPMENT

Ruler, tracing paper, $\frac{1}{2}$ cm and 1 cm squared paper, blank A4 paper, mirror, coloured pencils, scissors, compasses, 9-pin (or larger) nailboard, elastic bands, glue.

For the Introductory activities: right-angle tester, string, card shapes, set square.

**7
W1**
2D Shape:
Line and
rotational
symmetry

**SM2c/
4 → 5**

**RS/D3
S/D1, 2
S/E1, 2**

Content

- Identification and drawing of axes of symmetry
- Completion of shapes given the axes of symmetry
- Rotational symmetry: finding the number of times a shape fits its own outline in one rotation.

Detailed notes

Introductory activity

Language of symmetry
Discuss the pictures at the top of Core Textbook page 7 together with any collected by the pupils. Use the discussion to highlight terminology such as axes, horizontal, vertical.

Equipment

Ruler, tracing paper, mirror.

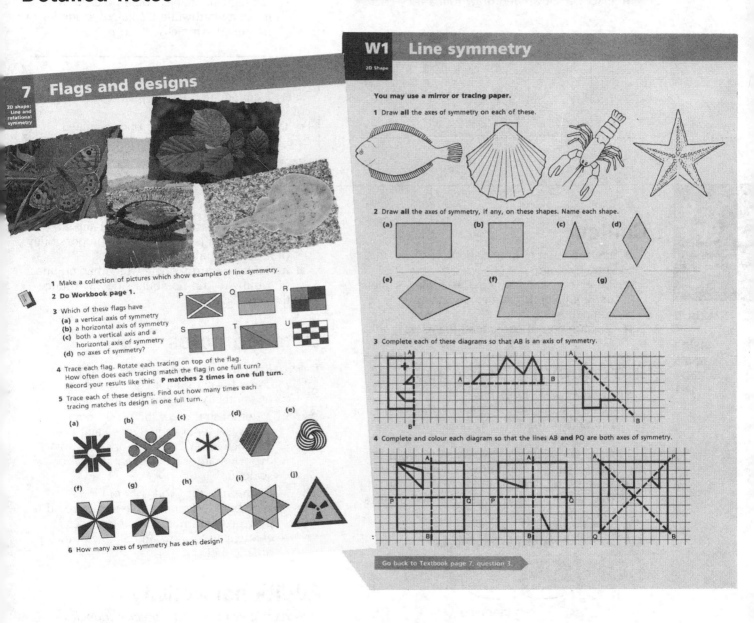

Detailed notes

Q1 Most objects when examined in detail will not be truly symmetrical (for example, photo of a face, even with centre hair parting), but some licence should be allowed in the collection.

W1, Q2 Although revision, the rectangle and parallelogram are likely to cause problems. If necessary, pupils can check by folding a paper shape.

W1, Q3 third part This line of symmetry may cause some difficulty. A mirror may be useful.

W1, Q4 An explanation may be required about using two axes of symmetry simultaneously. Some pupils may use different colours on the same diagram. Ensure that colour has not 'destroyed' the symmetry.

Q3 International code flags (see Heinemann Mathematics 7, Core Textbook page 63) and the *Highway Code* book contain symbols representing for example, single letters or whole sentences. The flags shown beside **Q3** do **not represent** the International code letters P, Q, R, ...

Q4 Tracing and 'fitting' has to include the colour matching.

8
2D Shape: Rotation

UA2c/4
SM2b,
3c/4

PM/D4
S/E2
PSE

Content

- Construction of shapes with rotational symmetry of order 4, using successive rotations of 90° about a vertex of a triangle and a kite.

Introductory activity

Making shapes with rotational symmetry
Demonstrate using a large card obtuse-angled triangle.

- Place as shown and draw round it.

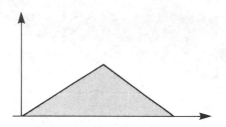

- Rotate successively through 90° drawing each new position.
- Starting with different vertices at the origin and different sides along the axis, different designs are produced.
- Each finished design has rotational symmetry of order 4.

Detailed notes

Q2g   The coloured design may match 1, 2 or 4 times in a complete rotation. This and subsequent shapes could be used to make a worthwhile display of examples of rotational symmetry.

Equipment

Ruler, 1 cm squared paper, plain paper, coloured pencils, scissors.
For the Introductory activity: obtuse-angled, card triangle.

9
W4
2D Shape:
Classification
of triangles by
sides

SM2bc/5

RS/D3
RS/E5
S/D1
I/E1

Content

- Interpretation of information presented in a Venn diagram
- Properties of right-angled, isosceles, scalene and equilateral triangles, including axes of symmetry
- Construction of equilateral triangles.

Introductory activities

1 Revision of Venn diagrams.

- Make a set of about 12 shapes from card, for example, 4 triangles, 4 squares and 4 rectangles.
  Have two large and two small versions of each shape, cut from two colours of card.
- Discuss the classification of these shapes (red shapes in a loop of string and triangles in a different loop.)

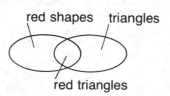

red shapes   triangles

red triangles

- The red triangles are now shown as an intersection in a Venn diagram.
- Each region in the diagram should be described precisely, for example, 'shapes which are red', 'shapes which are triangles', 'shapes which are triangles and red'.

2 Introduction of the scalene triangle

- Make several demonstration size triangles from card. Include isosceles, equilateral and right-angled triangles. Use them to revise identification and to test the equal sides and symmetry properties by fitting and turning the card shapes in their outlines. Mark equal sides and axes of symmetry. Right angles can be tested using a set square.

- Discuss the possibility of a right-angled triangle being isosceles but the impossibility of it being equilateral.
- Introduce a card triangle which has no lines of symmetry and no equal sides. Introduce the term scalene.

Detailed notes

Panel above Q1   Establish with pupils if necessary, the correct way to mark equal sides and axes of symmetry as shown in the panel.

W4, Q1   A demonstration of the use of tracing paper to identify equal sides and axes of symmetry may be necessary. The answers expected are isosceles, equilateral or scalene.

Q4   Before returning to Q4 from the Workbook, the more able pupils could be provided with ruler and compasses and challenged to draw an equilateral triangle of side 6 cm.

Additional activity

Constructing scalene and isosceles triangles
You could challenge some pupils to find out how to draw an isosceles triangle or a scalene triangle using ruler and compasses and then write brief but precise instructions for a neighbour to draw these shapes. These instructions should be discussed.

Equipment

Tracing paper, ruler, compasses, plain paper, coloured pencil.
For the Introductory activities: prepared card shapes, string, set square.

Content

- Interpretation of information presented in Venn diagrams
- Construction of obtuse- and acute-angled triangles, including axes of symmetry
- Plotting coordinate points
- Investigation: making different triangles on a 9-pin nailboard.

Introductory activities

1 Revision of acute and obtuse angles using a right-angle 'tester'

Pupils can make a right-angle 'tester' by tearing a corner from a sheet of paper. Perhaps, more interestingly, they could make a 'tester' by folding a circular piece of tissue paper in quarters. Acute and obtuse are then tested.

2 Introduction of acute-angled and obtuse-angled triangles

- Make several demonstration size triangles from card.
- Invite the pupils to 'test' the corners of the triangle for acute, obtuse, right angles.
- Discuss the results – a triangle may have three acute angles, or two acute and one right angle, or two acute and one obtuse angle. Introduce the terms 'acute-angled', 'right-angled' and 'obtuse-angled' (determined by the largest angle).

Detailed notes

W4, Q2 The pupils may use their right-angle testers.
Tracing paper may be used to identify any axes of symmetry.

Q5a It may be necessary to stress that separate diagrams are expected.

Q6 Pupils need to discuss how to interpret the phrase '**different** triangles'. It is suggested that they be allowed to include large and small versions of the same type of triangle but not different orientations.

Additional activities

1 More triangles on the nailboard

The investigation in Q6 may be extended. For example, having found the right-angled isosceles triangle shown they could attempt to find how many of this specific triangle could be made in different positions on the board. This could be repeated for other triangles in order to find out 'the total number of triangles that can be made on a 9-pin nailboard'. The opportunity will arise to use the term 'congruent' if desired.

2 Classification of triangles in a Venn diagram

Some pupils may be interested in developing a Venn diagram to show the full classification of all seven types of triangle.

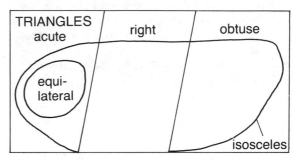

Equipment

Tracing paper, $\frac{1}{2}$ cm squared paper, 9-pin nailboard (or larger board marked off to this size), elastic bands.
For the Introductory activities: right-angle 'tester', card triangles.

10
W4
2D Shape: Classification of triangles b angles

UA2b/5
SM2ab/5

A/C2
RS/D3
S/D1
PM/D3
I/E1
PSE

11
W20
W21
**2D Shape:
Construction
of shapes**

**UA2ac/5
SM2a/5**

**RS/D2, 3
RS/E2
PSE**

Content

- Construction of quadrilaterals on a nailboard and from pairs of congruent right-angled, equilateral and isosceles triangles
- Construction of pentagons from triangles and quadrilaterals
- Investigation: making quadrilaterals from pairs of congruent scalene triangles.

Organisation

- Although Q1–Q4 many be attempted individually some cooperative work, say in pairs, should be encouraged.
- Q5 and Q6 are intended to be attempted by pupils working in a group.

Introductory activity

Quadrilaterals from pairs of congruent triangles
- Make one demonstration size pair of identical right-angled scalene triangles. (The term 'congruent' may be used.) Discuss the different ways that they can be fitted together whole edge to whole edge to produce other shapes.
- Repeat for a pair of obtuse-angled isosceles triangles as in Q1.

Detailed notes

Q1 Encourage pupils to experiment with different possibilities for pairing triangles *before* glueing them in place.

Q2 Pupils should be familiar with most names but may be less confident with others such as V-kite and trapezium. Some of the quadrilaterals have no special name.

Q3, 4 Some of the shapes are used more than once. The composite shapes should be sketched *not* glued.

Additional activity

The Hexagon Challenge
Use the shapes from Q3.
- Find pairs of shapes that fit together to make a hexagon.
- Find three shapes that fit together to make a hexagon.
- Using ruler and compasses only, draw a hexagon into which you can fit exactly six of shape C.

Equipment

Scissors, glue, 9-pin nailboard (or large board marked off to this size), elastic bands, 1 cm squared paper.
For the Introductory activity: card triangles.

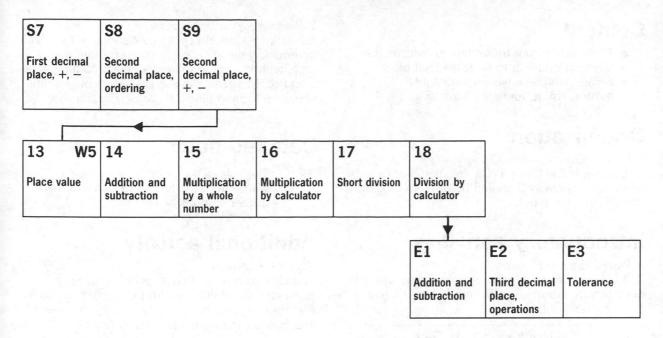

S7	S8	S9
First decimal place, +, −	Second decimal place, ordering	Second decimal place, +, −

13 W5	14	15	16	17	18
Place value	Addition and subtraction	Multiplication by a whole number	Multiplication by calculator	Short division	Division by calculator

E1	E2	E3
Addition and subtraction	Third decimal place, operations	Tolerance

CONTENT AND DEVELOPMENT

Core

Heinemann Mathematics 7 includes work on place value to thousandths and subtraction of two-place decimals, multiplication of two-place decimals by 2 to 10, 100 and by calculator, division of two-place decimals by 2 to 9 and by calculator, including interpretation of calculator answers and approximation to the nearest whole number and to the first decimal place.

In Heinemann Mathematics 8 *Decimals 1* contains work on:

- three-place decimal notation
- two-place decimals:
  - addition and subtraction
  - multiplication and division by single-digit whole numbers
  - multiplication and division using a calculator
- problem-solving activities.

Support

S7–S9 provide lead-in material and relate to Core Textbook pages 13 and 14. Similar support for the multiplication and division work on Core Textbook pages 15 to 18 is provided on S20 to S22 within the *Decimals 2* section.

Extension

The use of the calculator should be permitted throughout.

- Problem-solving activities using addition and subtraction of fractions and one- and two-place decimals
- The four operations using the third decimal place
- Using and finding averages
- Idea of tolerance using third decimal place.

National Curriculum (England and Wales)

UA2ad, 3d
N2ab, 3ce, 4ad
SM4ab

Mathematics 5–14 (Scotland)

RTN/D4   RTN/E2, 3   AS/D2
AS/E1, 2, 3   MD/D2, 3, 4
MD/E3, 4   ME/C6   ME/D1, 2, 3   O/D1
I/D1   I/E3   PSE   E+

RELATED ACTIVITIES

Decimals in the environment
Pupils could find examples of instances where values involving first, second and third decimal places are used in

- facts and figures
- national newspapers
- weather details
- sports data
- other subject areas.

It may be worth discussing how the number of decimal places relates to the context. For example:
one-place decimals: rounding of large numbers in national newspapers, £2.6 million
two-place decimals: money, a person's height, high and long jump
three-place decimals: speeds in skiing and motor racing.

EQUIPMENT

10 m tape, 2 metre sticks, calculator, a 'loaf' consisting of 10 square slices.

For the Introductory activities: stopwatch.

13
W5
Decimals 1:
Place value

N2a/5
SM4a/5

RTN/D4
RTN/E3
ME/D1, 2, 3
AS/E1, 2
O/D1

Content

- Place value from thousands to thousandths
- Decimal notation to three-decimal places
- Relationships between metric units:
  m/mm, km/m, tonne/kg, l/ml, kg/g.

Organisation

Class discussion of Introductory activity 1 is recommended before Q1–Q4 are attempted. Introductory activity 2 should be discussed before Q5–Q8 are attempted.

Introductory activities

1 Place value to thousands
If structured base 10 material is available, use it to demonstrate the ideas in Doug's Decimal Bakery on Core Textbook page 13.

Thousands	Hundreds	Tens	Units

Use class discussion to set the scene and to ensure that pupils realise that the 'loaf' is the basic unit.

2 Place value to thousandths
The bakery scenario could be developed by introducing the slice, finger and crouton, one at a time, with the appropriate decimal recording. Use a loaf of '10 slices'. A slice could be cut as in the scenario, to help pupils visualise the situation.

Detailed notes

W5 The role of the point to separate the whole from the fractional part may need further emphasis.

Additional activity

Kitchen measures
The dimensions of kitchen units are usually expressed in millimetres. You could ask pupils to find these specifications in brochures or adverts, and convert the measurements to metres.

Equipment

'Loaf' consisting of 10 square slices.

14
Decimals 1:
Addition and
subtraction

N3c/4

RTN/D4
AS/E1, 2
O/D1

Content

- Addition and subtraction to two-decimal places including money
- Place value to two-decimal places.

Introductory activities

1 My club colours
Ask pupils which clubs or organisations they have joined and follow this up with a discussion of club colours and their costs.

2 Walking times
Before tackling Q6, pupils could time each other walking over a fixed distance using a stopwatch, and then place the times in order. The four best times could be added together and this total compared against the totals of other groups.

Detailed notes

Q1 All answers should be given in pounds.

Q1e Further explanation of place value will be needed if the answer is incorrectly given as £4·8 or £4·80.

Q4 Explanation of the receipt having a hidden part and the term 'amount tendered' may be necessary.

Q5 Discuss the use of abbreviations in the marks table to show which country each judge represents.

Q6 Establish that the fastest time (smallest numerical value) is the winner.

Equipment

For Introductory activity 2: stopwatch.

Content

- Multiplication of one- and two-place decimals by single-digit whole numbers and multiples of 10
- Construction and use of a ready reckoner
- Interpretation of information presented in written and visual form.

Introductory activities

1 Club outings
Class discussion could include form of transport, distance travelled, the estimated cost per person, types of refreshments carried and so on.

2 Multiplication by multiples of 10
Revision of the technique of multiplying a whole number or decimal by a multiple of 10 may be necessary. For example:

$$0{\cdot}53 \times 40 = (0{\cdot}53 \times 10) \times 4$$
$$\text{or} \qquad (0{\cdot}53 \times 4) \times 10$$

Detailed notes

Q2, 3 The table completed in Q1 should be used as a ready reckoner.

Q7 Explanation of 'inside' may be necessary.

Equipment

None.

15
Decimals 1:
Multiplicatior
by a whole
number

N3c/
4 → 5

RTN/D4
MD/D2, 3
I/D1
O/D1

Content

- Multiplication of one- and two-place decimals by two-digit whole numbers using a calculator.

The use of a calculator allows pupils to concentrate on interpretive and other problem-solving skills.

Introductory activity

Diving scores
It may be necessary to discuss how scores are calculated from the judges marks. A dive of 2·1 is more demanding that one of 1·2. The greater the number representing the 'difficulty', the more demanding the dive.

Detailed notes

Q5 It may be necessary to discuss how to calculate the total weight of each group.

Q6 Initially a guess-and-check strategy may be used. A systematic consideration of possible combinations should be encouraged.

Equipment

Calculator.

16
Decimals 1:
Multiplicatior
by calculator

N3c/5

RTN/D4
MD/D4
PSE

Content

- Division of one- and two-place decimals by single digit whole numbers and 10.

Pupils are expected to use a written method for divisions involving money, weight, length, averages.

The language and recording of division used in earlier years of the Heinemann Mathematics course is described on page I2 of these notes.

Introductory activity

Running a restaurant
Discussion about restaurants should include ordering of food, sharing of tips, layout of tables, opening and closing times, average amount spent by customers, the weekly cost of fuel and so on.

Detailed notes

Q2 The difference between a '$\frac{1}{4}$ off' and '$\frac{1}{4}$ of' may need to be highlighted. Pupils may need to be reminded that a discount is subtracted.

Q4 Encourage pupils to draw annotated diagrams to help them visualise the problem.

Equipment

None.

17
Decimals 1:
Short divisior

UA3d/5
N3c/5

RTN/D4
MD/D3

18
Decimals 1:
Division by
calculator

N3ce/5

RTN/D4
MD/E4

Content

■ Division of whole numbers, one- and two-place decimals by one-, two- and three-digit whole numbers using a calculator.
The use of a calculator allows pupils to concentrate on interpretive and other problem-solving skills.

Detailed notes

Q2b   Pupils may divide either by 50 and then by 6, or directly by 300.

Q4a   Encourage systematic recording of answers.

Q5b   A trial-and-error approach is acceptable here.

Equipment

Calculator.

S7
Decimals 1:
First decimal
place, +, −

N2a, 3c/
4 →→ 5

RTN/D4
ME/C6
AS/D2

Content

■ Reading scales showing tenths
■ Ordering one-place decimals
■ Addition and subtraction of one-place decimals.

Introductory activity

Our weights
Some pupils are sensitive about their weights so here are some examples that could be used. Another difficulty is that most commercial bathroom scales weigh to the nearest half kilogram. If suitable scales are available and the pupils are willing to weigh themselves then use the real data.

Esther	57·4 kg	Karin	58·9 kg
Mark	65·3 kg	Lianne	61·7 kg
Saeeda	55·8 kg	Robin	54·3 kg

1 Order these people starting with the lightest.
2 Calculation of total weights and weight differences will give rise to addition and subtraction.
3 The average weight is 58·9 kg.

All recording should be rounded to the first decimal place.

Detailed notes

Q6   If necessary, draw attention to the fact that these are times and that the **smallest** numerical value is the fastest time.

Q6c   Help may be needed in interpreting this wording.

Equipment

None.

S8
Decimals 1:
Second
ecimal place,
ordering

N2b/4
SM4b/4

RTN/D4
ME/C6

Content

■ Reading scales showing hundredths
■ Ordering two-place decimals.

Introductory activity

Our classroom
The dimensions of the classroom, windows, cupboards and so on could be measured to the nearest centimetre and recorded in the decimal form.

Detailed notes

Q4   If necessary, encourage the pupils to use the scale shown in Q3.

Equipment

For the Introductory activity: 10 m tape.

Content

- Reading scales showing hundredths
- Addition and subtraction of two-place decimals.

Introductory activity

Our heights
Pupils could measure each others' heights to the nearest centimetre, record them in decimal form and find the differences in their heights.

Equipment

For the Introductory activity: 2 metre sticks taped to the wall.

Content

- Problem-solving activities using addition and subtraction of fractions and one- and two-place decimals.

Detailed notes

Triangle Trouble Puzzle 3 (numbers only provided)
Some or all of the following information may be given if difficulty is experienced:
- each side has a sum of 6·97
- the numbers at the vertices are 2·49, 0·92 and 3·18 (one, two or all three of these numbers may be given).

Equipment

None.

E1
Decimals 1: Addition and subtraction

UA2ad/5
N3c/5

RTN/E2
AS/D2
AS/E2
PSE
E+

Content

- The four operations using the third decimal place
- Using and finding averages.

Detailed notes

Q4
The phase 'half as much again' may require some clarification.

Q9b
Encourage pupil discussion.

Equipment

None.

Content

- Idea of tolerance using third decimal place.

Introductory activity

Made to measure
A discussion on the need for accuracy in manufacturing components will help to set the scene. The meanings of the words 'acceptable' and 'specification' should form part of the discussion. Pupils may have met this concept in other subject areas such as Craft and Design.

Equipment

None.

20	21	22
Tiling on grids	Escher-type tilings	Escher-type tilings

CONTENT AND DEVELOPMENT

Core

Heinemann Mathematics 7 deals with tilings of simple straight sided shapes, and explores the patterns created by arrangements of coloured tiles. Heinemann Mathematics 8 extends these ideas by

- examining tessellations of more complex shapes
- creating Escher-type tilings from simple basic shapes
- producing templates to create Escher-type tessellations.

National Curriculum (England and Wales)

UA2c,3c
SM2ab,3c

Mathematics 5–14 (Scotland)

RS/D2, 5
PM/D4
S/E2
PSE

RELATED ACTIVITIES

Tessellations around us
Pupils could be asked to look for examples of tessellations. Look at cultural differences such as Islamic, Roman, Spanish.

Examine the work of Escher, looking at reflection, perspective and tessellations. Colleagues in the Art department may be able to provide useful information.

Pupils could colour and display all tessellations produced.

EQUIPMENT

Coloured pencils, 1 cm isometric dot paper, 1 cm square dot paper, card, scissors, pencil, rubber, sticky tape, plain paper.

For the Introductory activity: sets of regular polygons.

Content

- Congruence
- Construction of tessellations on grids
- Different tessellations based on the same tile.

Introductory activity

Tessellating shapes
Revise the fact that the square, equilateral triangle and regular hexagon are the only three regular polygons which tessellate. It is worth demonstrating what happens when regular pentagons and octagons are used.

Detailed notes

20
Tessellations:
Tiling on grids

UA2c/4
SM2a/4

RS/D5
PM/D4
S/E2

| Panel above Q1 | The pictures provide a focus for discussion. Use this opportunity to revise the meaning of 'congruent'. |

| Q2 | Ensure pupils use the isometric paper like this |

and not like this

Equipment

Coloured pencils, 1 cm isometric dot paper, 1 cm square dot paper, card, scissors.
For the Introductory activity: sets of regular polygons.

Content

- Construction of Escher-type tessellations on grids by modifying squares and rectangles.

Introductory activity

Pupils should try to find out about the Dutch artist M.C. Escher. It may encourage pupils to tell them that they could be creating 'Birds' by the end of the unit.

Detailed notes

21
Tessellations:
Escher-type
tilings

SM2a,
3c/4

RS/D5
S/E2

| Q2, 3 | Curved parts should be drawn freehand. |

Equipment

Pencil, rubber, 1 cm square dot paper.

22
Tessellations:
Escher-type
tilings

UA3c/5
SM2ab,
3c/5

RS/D2, 5
PM/D4
S/E2
PSE

Content

- Construction of Escher-type pictures using a template, made by modifying rectangles, triangles and regular hexagons.

Additional activity

Comparing tessellations

Ask more able pupils if they can explain why in Q1 the tiles tessellated with each tile the same way up, but in Q2 alternate tiles had to be rotated 180° to tessellate.

Equipment

Card, scissors, sticky tape, plain paper, 1 cm isometric dot paper.

Detailed notes

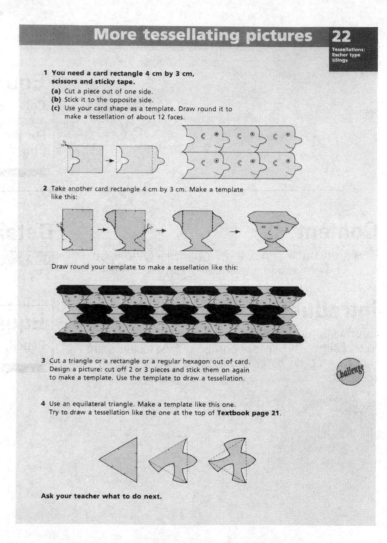

More tessellating pictures **22**
Tessellations:
Escher type
tilings

1 **You need a card rectangle 4 cm by 3 cm, scissors and sticky tape.**
   (a) Cut a piece out of one side.
   (b) Stick it to the opposite side.
   (c) Use your card shape as a template. Draw round it to make a tessellation of about 12 faces.

2 Take another card rectangle 4 cm by 3 cm. Make a template like this:

Draw round your template to make a tessellation like this:

3 Cut a triangle or a rectangle or a regular hexagon out of card. Design a picture: cut off 2 or 3 pieces and stick them on again to make a template. Use the template to draw a tessellation.

Challenge

4 Use an equilateral triangle. Make a template like this one. Try to draw a tessellation like the one at the top of **Textbook page 21**.

Ask your teacher what to do next.

Q3 Isometric dot paper could be used to make the regular hexagon.

Q4 Accuracy of measurement and positioning must be stressed. Isometric dot paper could simplify this task.

Cut-out 1 must be made centrally and positioned centrally as shown:

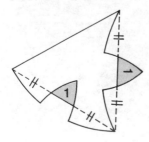

Alternatively, for pupils having difficulty, modify the measurements as shown:

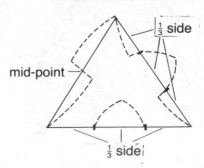

mid-point

$\frac{1}{3}$ side

$\frac{1}{3}$ side

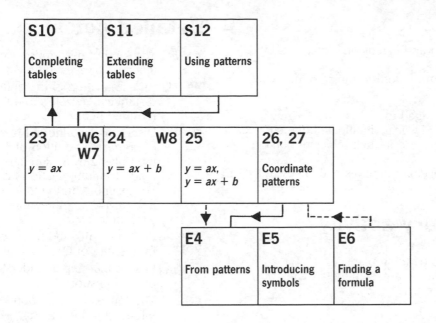

S10	S11	S12
Completing tables	Extending tables	Using patterns

23 W6 W7	24 W8	25	26, 27
$y = ax$	$y = ax + b$	$y = ax$, $y = ax + b$	Coordinate patterns

E4	E5	E6
From patterns	Introducing symbols	Finding a formula

CONTENT AND DEVELOPMENT

Core

Heinemann Mathematics 7 introduces simple relationships of the type $y = ax$ and $y = x \pm c$ expressed as word formulae. This work is done informally by looking at sets of number pairs.

Heinemann Mathematics 8 uses a more structured approach and includes

- recognition and extension of shape and number patterns
- word formulae of the type $y = ax$ and $y = ax + b$
- finding relationships between sets of x and y coordinates.

Support

S10–S12 provide a lead-in to the work of Core Textbook page 23.

Extension

E4–E6 provide further work on establishing both word and symbolic formulae of the type $y = ax \pm b$. They could be tackled either after Core Textbook page 25 or on completion of the Core work.

EQUIPMENT

Ruler, $\frac{1}{2}$ cm squared paper, tiles, counters, two differently coloured dice, spent matchsticks or similar sticks.

For the Related activity: 1 cm cubes.

National Curriculum (England and Wales)

UA2ab
A2b, 3ab

Mathematics 5–14 (Scotland)

FE/D1	FE/E4	PS/E1, 2
PM/D3	S/E2	PSE E+

RELATED ACTIVITIES

Patterns using cubes
1 cm cubes could be used for building and extending patterns. You could encourage pupils to make their own patterns then construct and extend tables. They may be unable to find word formulae to describe the patterns. Here are some examples of possible patterns.

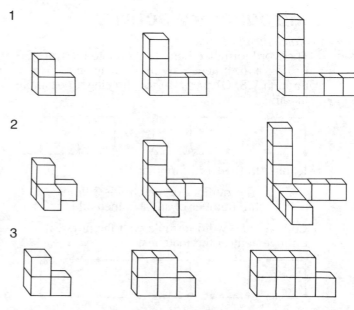

1

2

3

23
W6
W7
Word
formulae:
y = ax

A3b/
4 → 5

FE/D1

Content

- Recognition and extension of patterns of dots or lines
- Construction of word formulae of the type *y = ax*.

Pupils are encouraged to
- look at the physical situations in the contexts
- look for a pattern in their tables of number pairs
- predict subsequent entries and check by drawing.

Introductory activity

Plant pots
A box contains 8 bedding plants.
How many bedding plants will there be in 1, 2, 3, 4 boxes?

Pupils could
- record their results in a table like this

Number of boxes	1	2	3	4
Number of bedding plants	8	16	24	32

- extend the table to show the number of plants in 5 and 6 boxes
- state a word formula, for example 'The number of plants is eight times the number of boxes'
- describe the sequence in the bottom row of the table, for example 'The numbers go up in eights.'

Discussion should focus on the link between the increase each time and the multiplier in the word formula.

Detailed notes

W6, Q2 The kind of description expected is 'goes up by 2 each time'.

W6, Q3 An explanation of the phrase 'grid distance' between x and y may be required here.

W7, Q1 Discussion is required to emphasise that the repeated addition of 3 is the same as multiplying by 3. Reference could be made to multiplication table 'stations'. For example, in the three times table, 3, 6, 9, 12, . . ., the pattern increases by 3 each time.

W7, Q1b Complete only the first 5 entries initially in this part of Q1.

Q2 Ensure that pupils understand the context of the question.

Q3 The longest side of 'pond size 3' is intended to be 6 units. Some pupils may need guidance.

Equipment

None.

24
W8
Word
formulae:
y = ax + b

UA2ab/5
A3b/5

PS/E2
FE/D1
FE/E4
PSE

Content

- Recognition and extension of shape patterns
- Writing and using a word formula of the type *y = ax + b*.

Pupils have to investigate all the rectangular plots which can be surrounded by 20 slabs.

Introductory activity

Matchstick patterns
The word formulae here develop into the type *y = ax + b*. If necessary pupils may be led through W8, Q1 parts (a) to (d) using an example like this:

leading to the word formula:

The number of matches is 3 times the number of squares then add 1.

Compare the word formula with the physical arrangement of the matches:

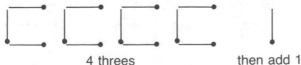

Detailed notes

Q2 The sketch shows a square bed of side 2 m.

Q2b, 3b, 4a These tables show an increase of 4 but give different formulae.

Q5 Pupils can use a sketch, table or a formula to find the solution. Reference back to Q2 should help.

Equipment

Spent matchsticks or similar sticks may be useful.

4 threes   then add 1

Content

- Recognition of pattern in seating arrangements
- Construction and use of word formulae of the type $y = ax + b$.

Introductory activities

Seating arrangements

1 4 desks could be used to demonstrate/investigate arrangements to seat exactly 6, 8, 9 or 10 pupils with/without the use of a wall.

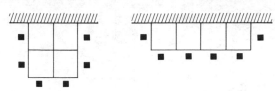

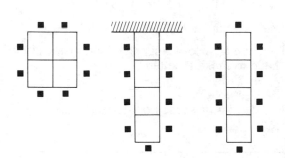

2 An additional problem could be set for pupils to investigate how 4 desks could be used to seat exactly 4 or 5 pupils. For this problem two walls would be required.

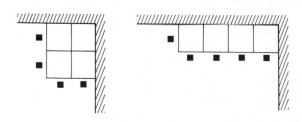

Detailed notes

Panel after Q3 | Pupils should always check their formula, by drawing if necessary.

Additional activities

1 The wedding problem
For a wedding the tables are arranged like this.

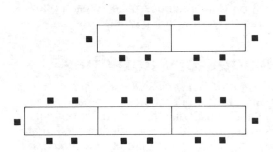

(a) Find a formula for the number of seats.
(b) Calculate how many guests can be seated at 15 tables.

2 Classroom seating
Ask pupils to design alternative seating plans for the classroom to include four or five groups of pupils. Groups can be of differing sizes.

Equipment

Tiles and counters may be useful.

25
Word formulae:
$y = ax$,
$y = ax + b$

A3b/5

PS/E2
FE/D1
FE/E4

26
27
Word
formulae:
Coordinate
patterns

A2b, 3b/
5 → 6

FE/D1
PM/D3
S/E2

Content

- Plotting and reading coordinate points
- Finding relationships between x and y coordinates as word formulae of the types $y = ax$ and $y = ax + b$
- Sequences.

Organisation

For Q3 on Core Textbook page 26 each pupil is required to work with a partner.

Introductory activities

1 Revision of first quadrant coordinates
The aim of the work on these two pages is to revise and consolidate first quadrant coordinate work. The points to be identified or plotted are based on patterns which are closely linked to the type found on Core Textbook pages 24 and 25. The following language and notation should be covered – first axis, second axis, axes, first and second coordinates, origin (0,0), plotting points (3,4), (2,7).

Special emphasis should be placed on points on the axes (3,0), (0,7).

2 Looking for a pattern in a set of coordinates
The scene for these two pages could be set by looking at an example similar to those in Q1 and Q2, covering the language and notation mentioned above. One such example could be

- Draw axes and plot several points which lie in a straight line, for example (1,3), (2,5), (3,7), (4,9).
- Draw a 'coordinate table' and introduce this term. Invite pupils to make the appropriate entries.
- Ask pupils to identify patterns in the coordinates. Highlight 'the increase in the second coordinate each time is . . .' and 'the second coordinate is . . . times the first coordinate then add . . .'

Detailed notes

26, Q3 Some pupils may need help to clarify the rules of the game.

Additional activity

Shape patterns
The ability to appreciate how shape patterns similar to those on Core Textbook page 27 are generated may be developed by the following activity.

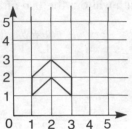

Use the shape shown above each time.

Describe how to change the coordinates of the shape to make a pattern
(a) in a row
(b) in a column
(c) sloping upwards from left to right.

Equipment

Ruler, $\frac{1}{2}$ cm squared paper, two differently coloured dice (red and blue preferred).

S10
Word
formulae:
Completing
tables

A2b/
3 → 4

FE/D1

Content

- Drawing dot and counter patterns and completing tables.

The work of the page is intended simply to give practice in the extension of patterns and the completion of tables. Pupils are *not* expected to find a formula.

Detailed notes

Q4 Pupils should use a pencil to draw the patterns. If pupils find difficulty in drawing the patterns, direct them to put the first dot immediately under the number. This should ensure enough space for each pattern.

Equipment

At least 11 counters.

Content

- Drawing tile patterns to generate a sequence and continuing the sequence.

Pupils could be asked to explain how they extended each table.

Equipment

Red and white tiles may be useful.

S11
Word formulae: Extending tables

A2b/4

FE/D1

Content

- Constructing tables from situations and completing a word formula.

Detailed notes

Panel after Q1 You should point out that 'the increase each time' is the same number as the one that you multiply by in the word formula.

Equipment

None.

S12
Word formulae: Using patterns

**A3b/
4 → 5**

FE/D1

Content

- Recognition and extension of patterns of shapes
- Construction of word formulae of the type $y = ax \pm b$.

Pupils should compare their word formulae with the physical arrangements of the disco lights.

Organisation

For Q3 each pupil is required to work with a partner.

Detailed notes

Q2c This is the first example of a word formula of the type $y = ax - b$.

Equipment

$\frac{1}{2}$ cm squared paper.

E4
Word formulae: From patterns

**A3b/
5 → 6**

FE/E4

Content

- Construction of symbolic formulae of the type $y = ax \pm b$ derived from word formulae
- Problem solving requiring a methodical approach.

Detailed notes

Panel after Q2 Pupils may write a symbolic formula without a word formula but they should state what each letter represents.

Equipment

None.

E5
Word formulae: Introducing symbols

**A3ab/
5 → 6**

FE/E4
PS/E1

Content

- Recognition and extension of shape patterns
- Construction of word and symbolic formulae of the type $y = ax \pm b$.

Introductory activity

Slabs
This design of grey and white slabs can be used to set the scene.

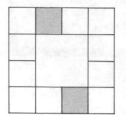 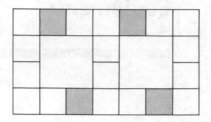 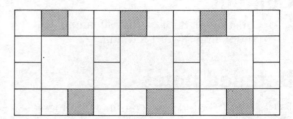

Ask pupils to draw the next pattern and find a formula connecting the number of flower beds and the number of grey slabs. They should construct a table, word formula and symbolic formula as follows:

Number of flower beds (f)	1	2	3	4
Number of grey slabs (g)	2	4	6	8

Number of grey slabs is 2 times the number of flower beds or $g = 2f$.

Pupils should then repeat the process for the white slabs, giving $w = 6f + 4$.

Additional activity

Creating tile patterns
Repeat Q3 introducing a third colour.

Equipment

None.

Detailed notes

Q2c Note that the number of white tiles is a constant, $w = 10$.

Q3 The pupils' designs could be tried with others in the class.

Some of their designs may not give simple formulae of the type $y = ax \pm b$.

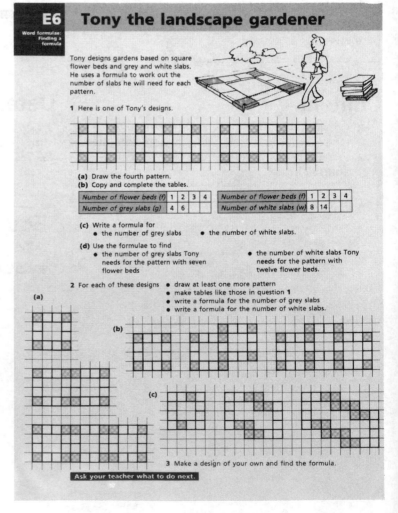

28	29	30	31 W9	32	
Lifescapes Exhibition Centre	The Halls at Lifescapes	Forthcoming attractions	Diary of events	What's On Today	▶

33 W10	34 W11	35 W22 36	37 W12 38	39
Basketball competition	The basketball finals	Fabric and Fashion Exhibition	Judo	Lifescapes car parks

CONTENT AND DEVELOPMENT

Core

General advice concerning the purpose of and management of an 'extended context' can be found on page 16 of these notes.

Lifescapes Exhibition Centre simulates the events in the calendar of a modern exhibition and conference centre. Activities revolve around

- the centre itself and its site
- a typical range of events occurring over one month or on one day
- individual events, competitions and exhibitions.

The mathematical content includes

- calendar work, time durations using 24-hour notation
- scale drawing
- specifying location, enlargement of shape, translation and reflection
- interpretation and construction of graphs
- carrying out a survey
- operations using whole numbers and money, simple fractions of a quantity
- problem solving
  - interpretation of information presented in written, tabular and visual form
  - recording of findings and their presentation in written and visual form
  - systematic listing, trial and improvement strategies.

National Curriculum (England and Wales)

UA2ac, 3bd, 4ac
N3ce, 4a
SM3bd, 4ad
HD2abf

Mathematics 5–14 (Scotland)

C/D1	D/C2	I/E1, 3	ME/E2
PFS/E1, 3	T/C4	FPR/C1	AS/D3
MD/C3	MD/D4	S/E2	PM/C1
PSE	E+		

RELATED ACTIVITIES

Visit to an exhibition centre
It may be possible to arrange a class visit to an exhibition centre. The pupils can then gain personal experience of its size, shape and layout, and how different events can occur simultaneously. Leaflets giving information about the centre itself and any events occurring during the visit could be brought back to school. Comparisons can then be made between the real and simulated exhibition centres.

Clearly within this context there are many possibilities to develop cross curricular work.

EQUIPMENT

Calculator, metre stick or long metric tape, calendar, coin, $\frac{1}{2}$ cm or 1 cm or 2 cm isometric paper, $\frac{1}{2}$ cm and 1 cm squared paper, blank paper (A4), coloured paper (approx. A5), paper for wall posters, coloured pencils, scissors, glue.

For Additional activities: local maps, knitting pattern booklets.

28

Extended
context 1:
Lifescapes
Exhibition
Centre

UA2c,
3d/4
SM4a/5

ME/E2

Content

- Specifying location (position fixing)
- Interpretation of information presented in visual form
- Estimation, measurement and calculation of rectangular areas in square metres.

Organisation

Some consideration should be given to the best time for the practical work in Q5.

Introductory activity

Introduction of the extended context
In a class discussion consider what an exhibition centre is; have any pupils visited one, what kind of exhibition was being held, what sort of things did they see?

Discuss the plan of the centre, in particular noting that the five exhibition halls are different sizes. Why should this be so? Emphasise the widely varied nature of events that can be accommodated, for example, from a computer exhibition to a cat show to a motor show.

The opportunity could be taken to locate features on the plan using position-fixing pairs such as E2.

Detailed notes

Q3 Pupils' responses could contribute to further class discussion.

Q4 The effect of perspective adds to the difficulty. A reasonable estimate would be 'A bit more than a quarter (3750 m^2), say about 4000 m^2.'

Q5 Measure length and breadth or other dimensions as appropriate to the nearest metre.

Additional activity

Find your street
Local maps could be used and the pupils asked to identify the grid boxes containing their own street or house, and other well-known local sights.

Equipment

Metre stick or long metric tape, calculator.
For the Additional activity: local maps.

29

Extended
context 1:
The Halls at
Lifescapes

UA2c3d/5
SM4d/5 → 6

PFS/E1
I/E1

Content

- Interpretation of information presented in written form
- Area of a rectangle.

Introductory activity

How large are the Halls?
Individual pupils could read aloud the descriptions of the Halls to aid interpretation. Discussion should cover the sizes of the various Halls, relating them to sizes known to the pupils. Their floor areas could be compared with areas in the school, for example the classroom, assembly hall, dining hall, hockey or football pitches. It would be worthwhile to estimate the number of classrooms which would 'fit' each Hall. Thereafter pupils might be able to suggest types of events which could be held in each Hall giving due consideration to length, breadth, headroom, seating capacity, etc.

Detailed notes

**Q2,
Hall 3** This area has to be *calculated*.

Q2 The information in the table should be checked for accuracy, particularly the area of Hall 3. This is needed for Core Textbook page 30.

Equipment

None.

Content

- Interpretation of information presented in tabular and written form
- The use of calendars – dates
- Presentation of findings in written and visual form.

Organisation

Group discussion would be desirable, particularly for Q3 and Q4.

Detailed notes

Q1 It may be helpful to discuss some of the dimensions in the table completed for Q2 on Core Textbook page 29. For example, which Hall is longest/has greater area?

The key, using the strategy of elimination, is to place the Circus in Hall 4.

Q2 The number of days includes the starting and finishing dates. A calendar may be helpful to some pupils.

Q3b, part 3 The solution is not unique. Reasons could be, for example:

Hall 4 – larger, greater capacity, etc.
Hall 3 – nearer to requested date, smaller and therefore more economical.

Equipment

Calendar, paper for a wall poster.

Content

- Interpretation of information presented in tabular and written form
- The use of calendars – dates
- Presentation of findings in written form.

Introductory activity

What's on and when
The January diary should be discussed to clarify the nature of the work on the page. Questions similar to Q1 to Q6 could be asked.

Detailed notes

Q8b A possible answer is to visit the centre when none of these three events is on, thus being 'fair' to each boy.

W9, Q1 Pupils should work in pencil in the first instance in case of error. When the diary is complete it can then be coloured in a format similar to that on Core Textbook page 31.

W9, Q2 The solution is not unique. Note that two events have to be allocated to Hall 1.

Equipment

Coloured pencils.

32
Extended
context 1:
What's on
today

UA3d/5
SM3b/
5 → 6
HD2ab/4;
2f/5

C/D1
D/C2
I/E1
PSE
E+

Content

- Shape enlargement and construction
- Systematic listing of possible outcomes
- Interpretation of a pie chart
- Carrying out a survey and displaying the data as a bar graph.

Organisation

Q6 requires a class survey. One group could be asked to collect data from the other groups and organise it for all to use.

Additional activity

Badges and logos
Pupils could cut out pictures of well-known badges and logos from newspapers and magazines and bring them to school. These could be used for wall display, and the more simple ones could be enlarged.

Equipment

$\frac{1}{2}$ cm or 1 cm or 2 cm isometric paper, 1 cm square paper, coloured pencils.

Detailed notes

Q1a Pupils choosing 1 cm or 2 cm paper should have little difficulty. Pupils using $\frac{1}{2}$ cm paper may need more precise instructions.

Q1b The badges designed could be added to the wall display.

Q2b Encourage pupils to list the choices systematically.

Q4 Calculations such as $\frac{3}{20}$ of 200 are not intended. Pupils should first work out that each division represents ten visitors.

Q5 If the plan on Core Textbook page 28 is consulted, less obvious possibilities (helicopter, boat) may be revealed.

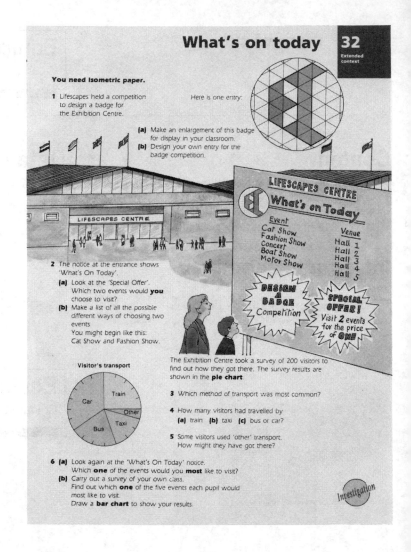

Content

- Interpretation of information presented in written form
- Addition, subtraction and averages using whole numbers
- Simple fractions of a quantity.

A calculator should not be necessary but it may be a useful time-saver.

Introductory activities

1 Leagues

Initial discussion with the class or group should set the scene for the work based on the Basketball competition which appears on Core Textbook pages 33 and 34, and W10 and W11. What is a league? How does it work? In some leagues teams meet once, in others they meet 'home and away'. Which leagues do the pupils know of? Why have leagues at all?

33
W10
Extended context 1: Basketball competition

UA3d/5
N3c,4a/5

FPR/C1
I/E1, 3
PSE

2 A mini-league

The following set of league results could be listed, discussed and a league table drawn up. For each game played (P), two points are allocated for a win (W), one for a draw (D) and no points for a game lost (L). Rovers are placed ahead of United because of their better 'goal difference'. This means that although they have the same number of points their 'difference between goals for (F) and goals against (A)' is greater.

Rovers 3	City 0
United 3	City 1
City 2	Rovers 1
United 1	Rovers 1
City 2	United 3
Rovers 2	United 1

	P	W	D	L	F	A	Pts
Rovers	4	2	1	1	7	4	5
United	4	2	1	1	8	6	5
City	4	1	0	3	5	10	2

Equipment

None.

Detailed notes

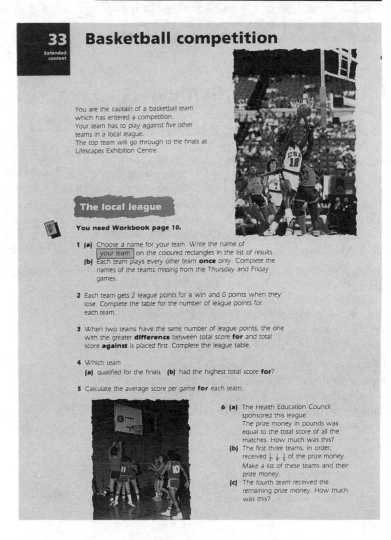

Q1b Pupils having difficulty may be assisted if asked, 'Which team must be the one to play against the Eagles on Friday?'

Q2 Winners and losers are identified from match scores.

Q3 Goal differences for teams with equal points must be calculated *before* making the entries in the table.

Q4 The information that only the top team qualifies is in the panel at the top of the page.

Q5 The question is asking for the average number of points scored per game by each team – divide the total number of points scored by 5.

Q6 It is a useful check to verify that the total scores 'for' and 'against' are equal.

UA2ac/5
N3e/4

AS/D3
MD/D4
E+

Content

- Interpretation of information presented in written form
- Whole number operations using a calculator
- Presentation of findings in written form.

Introductory activity

It's a knockout
Discuss how a knock-out competition is run and contrast this with a league system. A short knock-out competition of Nim or Noughts-and-Crosses could be carried out and results displayed. If there are not the appropriate number of pupils to pair up, it may be necessary to discuss what is meant by a 'bye' into the second round.

Which sports (for example, tennis) and which competitions (for example, the Football Association cup) use the knock-out system? The 1990 finals of the football World Cup used a mixture of leagues and knock-out rounds.

Detailed notes

Q1a It may be more convenient to provide the seven other names.

Q1b Some pupils may need further explanation of this procedure.

Q2, 3 Each score has to be entered in the box next to the team's name.

Q5b A trial and improvement approach is the most likely strategy here.

Q7 The necessary information has to be interpreted from the poster at the top of W11.

Equipment

Calculator, sheets of paper, scissors, coin.

35
36
W22
Extended
Context 1:
Fabric and
Fashion
Exhibition

UA3d/5

I/E1
S/E2

Content

- Interpretation of information in written and visual form (codes for knitting patterns)
- Translation and reflection of shapes (designs for T-shirts).

Introductory activities

1 Knitting patterns
Some knitting patterns may be presented in coded diagram form as in Q1. Here *row 1* is at the bottom of the diagram. Others may use a coded word form as in the centre panel, where *row 1* is at the top of a list of instuctions. This difference is a likely source of difficulty which you may wish to point out before the work is attempted. However, it will be challenging to more able pupils not to have this help.

Pupils may find it interesting to view some real pattern booklets. In order to simplify the work using the coded word form the even-numbered rows have been reversed from the normal order in knitting patterns.

2 T-shirt designs
Less able pupils should benefit from a demonstration of the process of creating a design. A colourful product should be created if the starting shape is large and is coloured differently on each side.

Detailed notes

Q2 An explanation of the bubbles 'Extend to x rows . . .' is likely to be necessary.

Q2b Alert pupils to the need to leave enough space to extend the sweater designs both across *and* up.

Q5, 7 The completed design could be used in a wall display.

Equipment

$\frac{1}{2}$ cm squared paper, pencils in three different colours, coloured paper (approx. A5), scissors, glue.
For Introductory activity 1: knitting pattern booklets.

Content

- Scale drawing and interpretation of plans
- Specifying location (position fixing)
- Trial and improvement strategy
- Addition and multiplication of money.

Introductory activity

About judo

A brief discussion with the class or group may help to set the scene for the work on these pages. Do any pupils take part in judo? Where? In a competition? The picture at the top of Core Textbook page 37 should be used to highlight the layout of a competition area.

Detailed notes

Q1 Pupils should work in pencil initially.

Q2 The mats should be clearly marked, then coloured and finally counted.

Q4 Three contest areas are possible, giving three competition areas only when safety areas are shared. Pupils should work in pencil initially.

Q5 Discussion of the method of identifying the position of seats on the W12 plan may be necessary.

Q8 The distance should be measured from the centre of the seat (square). It may be helpful to mention 'the distance as the crow flies'.

Q10 Some pupils may not realise unless prompted that the seat numbers are inclusive.

Q11 A trial-and-improvement strategy might be used. Encourage pupils to record systematically, for example:

8 seats at £10 ⟶ £80

7 seats at £10 + 1 at £7 ⟶ £77 etc.

Equipment

Red, blue and green coloured pencils.

UA2c,
3d/5
N4a/5
SM3d/5

PFS/E3
PM/C1
MD/C3
PSE

39
Extended
context 1:
Lifescapes
car parks

UA3d/5
N3c/4

I/E1
T/D1, 2
PSE

Content

- Interpretation of information presented in written or visual form
- Calculation of time durations involving 24-hour notation
- Addition and multiplication of money.

Introductory activity

Car parking charges
The location of the car parks can be discussed by referring to the plan of the Exhibition Centre on Core Textbook page 28. Many pupils should be able to describe how different car parks charge. Some discussion of the picture at the top of Core Textbook page 39 is necessary in order to establish how this car park operates, in particular

- the charge system and
- the information provided on a ticket.

Equipment

Calculator.

Detailed notes

Q2a For the last ticket the time difference is through midnight.

Q2b The two tickets must have the IN and OUT times in common.

Q3 Some pupils will simply calculate 6016 − 4417 and so be one car short.

Q7 Pupils may need to be told that the numbers show the number of tickets in each part of the box.

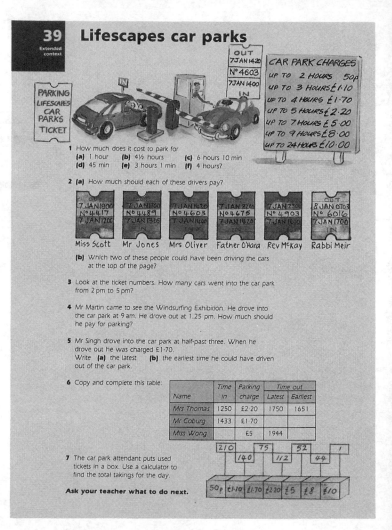

39 Lifescapes car parks

CAR PARK CHARGES
UP TO 2 HOURS 50p
UP TO 3 HOURS £1·10
UP TO 4 HOURS £1·70
UP TO 5 HOURS £2·20
UP TO 7 HOURS £5·00
UP TO 9 HOURS £8·00
UP TO 24 HOURS £10·00

1 How much does it cost to park for
(a) 1 hour (b) 4½ hours (c) 6 hours 10 min
(d) 45 min (e) 3 hours 1 min (f) 4 hours?

2 (a) How much should each of these drivers pay?

Miss Scott   Mr Jones   Mrs Oliver   Father O'Hara   Rev McKay   Rabbi Meir

(b) Which two of these people could have been driving the cars at the top of the page?

3 Look at the ticket numbers. How many cars went into the car park from 2 pm to 5 pm?

4 Mr Martin came to see the Windsurfing Exhibition. He drove into the car park at 9 am. He drove out at 1.25 pm. How much should he pay for parking?

5 Mr Singh drove into the car park at half-past three. When he drove out he was charged £1·70.
Write (a) the latest (b) the earliest time he could have driven out of the car park.

6 Copy and complete this table:

Name	Time in	Parking charge	Time out Latest	Time out Earliest
Mrs Thomas	1250	£2·20	1750	1651
Mr Coburg	1433	£1·70		
Miss Wong		£5	1944	

7 The car park attendant puts used tickets in a box. Use a calculator to find the total takings for the day.

Ask your teacher what to do next.

210 75 52 1
140 112 44
50p £1·10 £1·70 £2·20 £5 £8 £10

DETOURS IN PART 1

General advice about using the Detours can be found on page T6 of these Notes.

6
W3
Detour:
Flowcharts

UA3ab/6
N3a/4

I/E1
AS/C1
MD/C1
PSE

Content

- Interpretation of flowcharts
- Construction of flowcharts using trial and improvement
- Mental calculation using whole numbers.

Detailed notes

Panel above Q1 This flowchart could be discussed using several different starting numbers.

W3, Q1 The answers should be related to the starting numbers in each example.

Q2 Some pupils may find it helpful to copy the flowchart boxes provided, cut them out and then order them.

Additional activity

An unusual graph
Ask pupils to copy and complete this table for the flowchart in Q3 of Core Textbook page 6 and then draw a graph of the results.

Starting number	0	1	2	3	4	5	6	7	8	9	10	11	12	13	14	15
Answer	6	9														

A discontinuity occurs when the starting number is 8.

Equipment

Scissors.

12
Detour:
Mental
practice

N3ab/4

AS/D1
MD/D1

Content

- Mental addition of two-digit whole numbers using alternative methods
- Mental multiplication of money using alternative methods.

Detailed notes

Panels above Q1 and Q2 Discuss the methods illustrated with the pupils and encourage them to suggest their own alternative methods.

Additional activity

Working mentally
Pupils could be asked to investigate possible mental methods for some other calculations, for example

- adding/subtracting 19, 29, 39, . . .
- multiplying by 10, 5 and 100, 50.

Equipment

None.

19
Detour:
Checking
calculations

N3c,
4ad/5

I/E3
AS/D3
MD/E4

Content

- The four operations with whole numbers and decimals using a calculator
- Checking addition and multiplication by reordering
- Checking subtraction and division using their inverse operation.

Introductory activity

Reverse the order
Pupils could be asked to investigate calculations like the following

$8 + 5 =$	$8 - 5 =$	$8 \times 5 =$	$8 \div 5 =$
$5 + 8 =$	$5 - 8 =$	$5 \times 8 =$	$5 \div 8 =$

and state for which operations a change in the order of the numbers affects the result.

Detailed notes

Q5 Some pupils may need to be reminded how to find the volume of a cuboid.

Panels above Q6 These inverse operation relationships should be discussed after first considering some simpler examples.

Equipment

Calculator.

33

Content

■ Enlargement of shapes using a grid with larger squares.

Introductory activity

Enlarging a shape
Show pupils how to enlarge a shape like the one below (left) by transferring it to 1 cm squared paper (right). Sloping lines may cause some difficulty. They could be drawn after counting squares horizontally and vertically from one end of the line to the other, for example 'right 2 then down 2'.

Detailed notes

Last two pictures A different approach is appropriate for these pictures. Start at any square on the given picture and copy it on the larger grid; continue round the drawing enlarging square by square.

Equipment

Coloured pencils, 1 cm squared paper.

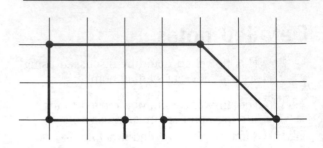

S13
Detour:
Distance and
direction

UA3d/
4 → 5

PM/C2

Content

■ Interpretation of coded instructions for generating 'spiral' patterns.

Detailed notes

Q1 It may be necessary to stress that the instructions in the table have to be repeated until 'stop' is reached.

Additional activities

1 Clockwise spirals
Change the direction of the arrows to:

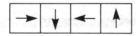

2 Isometric spirals
Investigate spirals like this:

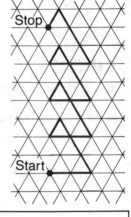

Equipment

Ruler, $\frac{1}{2}$ cm squared paper.

E7
Detour:
Half-turn
symmetry
investigation

UA2c/6
SM3c/5

PM/D4
S/E1, 2
PSE

Content

■ Construction of crossword grids using half-turn symmetry.
In this investigation a number of problem-solving skills are used.

Introductory activity

Crossword rules
This activity should be carried out *before* the pupils read the instructions on the page.

Pupils could bring in crosswords from newspapers or magazines and investigate their symmetry properties.

Alternatively a worksheet could be prepared showing crossword grids, three with half-turn symmetry labelled 'correct', and three which are not symmetrical labelled 'incorrect'. These can be investigated by the pupils leading to the conclusion that the grids labelled 'correct' are those which have half-turn symmetry.

Detailed notes

Q2 It is possible to produce many symmetrical patterns that comply with the rules stated but which would not make good crossword grids. For example, the 7 by 7 grid below, which has 12 black squares, would be very difficult to construct as a crossword puzzle although it does have 7 across clues and 7 down clues.

Equipment

Ruler, $\frac{1}{2}$ cm squared paper, tracing paper.
For the Introductory activity: prepared worksheet.

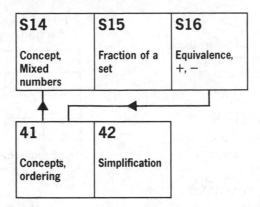

S14	S15	S16
Concept, Mixed numbers	Fraction of a set	Equivalence, +, −

41	42
Concepts, ordering	Simplification

CONTENT AND DEVELOPMENT

Core

Heinemann Mathematics 7 deals with equivalence, addition and subtraction of halves and quarters, multiplication of a fraction/mixed number by a whole number and a fraction of a whole number.

This section of Heinemann Mathematics 8 consolidates and extends the previous work and covers:

- informal multiplication and division with fractions
- ordering fractions using equivalence
- one quantity as a fraction of another quantity
- expressing a fraction in its simplest form.

Fractions 2 in *Part 3* extends the multiplication of fractions and shows how to change from fractions to decimals. The corresponding extension material deals with addition and subtraction of fractions.

Support

S14–S16 provide lead-in work to Core Textbook page 41.

National Curriculum (England and Wales)

N2b, 3c
HD2f

Mathematics 5–14 (Scotland)

I/C1
RTN/D3   **RTN/E2**
FPR/C1

RELATED ACTIVITIES

1 Fraction games
There are many commercial matching games available which provide useful practice in fractional notation, for example, snap and dominoes.

2 Computer software
Many computer programs provide similar practice.

EQUIPMENT

Coloured pencils.

For the Introductory activities: prepared diagrams or worksheet, paper strips, cut-out card 'pies'.

Content

- Informal multiplication and division using simple fractions and mixed numbers
- Ordering fractions using equivalence.

Introductory activities

The approach here is intended to be informal, but before pupils attempt the page they may need to revise some or all of the following.

- A bar of chocolate has 8 equal portions.
  Each portion is ☐ of a bar.
  Half a bar has 4 portions.
  Two bars have 16 portions.

- If a cup holds ☐ litre then 1 litre fills 5 cups
                                    and 2 litres fill 10 cups.

- Relative size of fractions:

  A ☐ litre cup holds less than a ☐ litre cup since
  1 litre fills six ☐ litre cups but only five ☐ litre cups.

- Equivalence of fractions:
  A fraction board can help show equivalence.

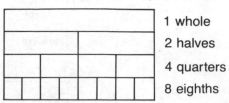

To change the 'name' of a fraction multiply both numerator and denominator by the same number.

$$\frac{1}{2} = \frac{1 \times 4}{2 \times 4} = \frac{4}{8}$$

Detailed notes

Q1c, d Some pupils may give these fractions in simplest form.

Q5 Some pupils may need help to realise that 6 slices represents $\frac{1}{4}$ of the full tray.

Equipment
None.

Content

- One quantity as a fraction of another and simplifying
- Expressing a fraction in its simplest form.

Detailed notes

Panel above Q1 The main discussion points are highlighted in this example.

Panel above Q5 It is important that pupils realise that the numerator and the denominator must be in the same units.

Q6, Table 4 bill The total has to be converted to pence before attempting to simplify.

Equipment
None.

Content

- Recognition and representation of simple fractions of shapes
- Informal conversion of mixed numbers to improper fractions
- Reading mixed numbers represented by bar graphs.

Introductory activities

Fractions of shapes
- Use strips of paper divided into equal parts to revise the concept of a fraction.

- Use diagrams of different shapes.

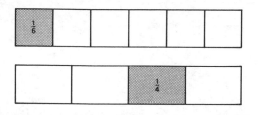

- Use similar diagrams for numerators greater than 1, for example:

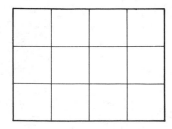

S14
Fractions 1: Concept, Mixed numbers

N2b/4
HD2f/3

I/C1
RTN/D3

- For mixed numbers use, for example:

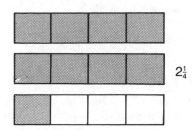

$2\frac{1}{4}$

and note that $2\frac{1}{4} = \frac{9}{4}$

Detailed notes

Q1 Fractions may be expressed in simplest form or left unsimplified.

Q3 The first and last shields should each have one section uncoloured. The other shields should be completely coloured.

Q5 Ensure that pupils notice that Olaf's recipe uses *quarter* hornfuls and Haakon's recipe uses *fifths*. Encourage pupils to enter mixed numbers in the table rather than improper fractions.

Equipment

Coloured pencils.
For the Introductory activities: prepared strips of paper.

Content

- Concept of a fraction of a set
- Word problems requiring the calculation of a fraction $(\frac{1}{2}, \frac{1}{3}, \frac{1}{4},)$ of a quantity.

Introductory activities

1 Fraction of a set using diagrams
Prepare diagrams and ask pupils to shade selected fractions without counting squares. For this diagram $\frac{1}{2}$ or $\frac{1}{3}$ or $\frac{1}{4}$ are suitable.

Discuss the number of squares and the number shaded, then introduce the recording

$\frac{1}{2}$ of $12 = 6$ and so on.

S15
Fractions 1: Fraction of a set

N3c/
4 → 5

RTN/D3
FPR/C1

2 Fraction of a set using division
Consider the diagram in Introductory activity 1 and establish how to find $\frac{1}{2}$ of 12 and so on, without a diagram.

Pupils should realise that $\frac{1}{2}$ of 12 can be found as $12 \div 2$ and so on.

Detailed notes

Q1 It is not intended that the equivalence of, for example, $\frac{1}{2}$ and $\frac{3}{6}$ be highlighted at this point.

Q2 Each fraction of a set should be found by mental division.

Q3c This may prove difficult because of the different nature of the question.

Equipment

Red, green, blue coloured pencils.
For the Introductory activities: paper diagrams or worksheets.

S16
Fractions 1:
Equivalence,
+, −

**N2b/
4 → 5**

RTN/D3

Content

- Equivalence of fractions
- Addition and subtraction of mixed numbers involving halves and quarters.

Organisation

Introductory activity 2, which revises addition and subtraction of halves and quarters, is probably better done when pupils have completed Q2.

Introductory activities

1 Revision of equivalence
A worksheet could be prepared containing blank shields similar to those in Q1. Pupils could use different colours to identify various fractions of each shield, for example:

shade $\frac{6}{8}$ blue

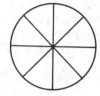

Although pupils may recognise the equivalent fraction by inspection they should be encouraged to do the 'formal' division of both numerator and denominator by the same number.

2 Revision of addition and subtraction
No formal method of recording is expected. It is hoped that the pupils will have memorised the addition and subtraction facts for halves and quarters; however, it may be useful to revise using pictures of 'pies' or perhaps cardboard cut-outs to represent 'pies' and the required fractions of 'pie'. These could then be used by the pupils to answer the questions in a practical way, for example:

Hak

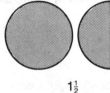 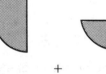 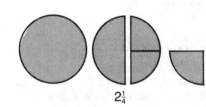

$1\frac{1}{2}$ + $\frac{3}{4}$ = $2\frac{1}{4}$

A set of 'pies' sufficient for the calculations would contain:
- 3 wholes
- 2 halves
- 2 quarters
- 2 three-quarters.

Detailed notes

Q3, 4   Some pupils may find the number line helpful.

Equipment

For the Introductory activities: prepared worksheet and cut-out card 'pies'.

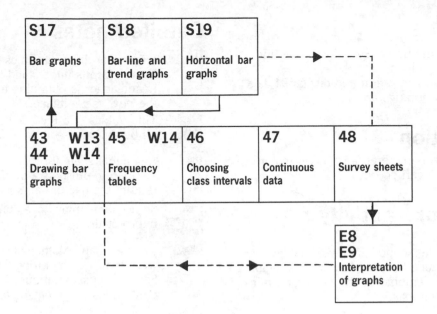

CONTENT AND DEVELOPMENT

Core

Heinemann Mathematics 7 contains work on bar and trend graphs, pie charts, average/mean, range, frequency tables and diagrams using class intervals for discrete data, or data treated as such.

Heinemann Mathematics 8 consolidates earlier work and introduces continuous data. It covers:

- interpretation and construction of bar, combined bar 'trend' graphs
- calculation of range and mean
- construction of frequency tables and diagrams using class intervals
- organisation and display of continuous data given/choosing class intervals
- design and completion of survey sheets for the collection of class data.

Graphs are used where appropriate in other sections of Heinemann Mathematics 8, for example pie charts are used in *Percentages 1*. *Handling data 2* covers work on interpretation and construction of straight-line and curved-line graphs, including conversion graphs.

Support

S17–S19 provide lead-in material. For some pupils the Support work may be used to parallel the work of the Core Textbook, leading directly to Core Textbook page 48.

Extension

E8 and E9 can be done either on completion of the section or after Core Textbook page 44.

National Curriculum (England and Wales)

UA4a
HD2abcdef

Mathematics 5–14 (Scotland)

C/D1	C/E1, 2	O/D1	O/E1	D/D1, 2
I/D1	I/E1, 2, 3	PSE	E+	

RELATED ACTIVITIES

Graphs in use
Graphs of all kinds are published regularly in newspapers, magazines and leaflets. Encourage pupils to collect as many examples as they can. These should be discussed and displayed. Graphs showing particularly useful or unusual features could be copied for the class and the information discussed.

Many examples of graphs can be found in other subject areas, especially geography and science.

Much of the data collected in this section could be used in conjunction with databases, spreadsheets and graph packages.

EQUIPMENT

Calculator, plain paper, 2 mm, $\frac{1}{2}$ cm, 1 cm squared paper, coloured pencils, personal scales, 2-metre tape measure.

For Additional activities: a seconds timer.

**43
44
W13
W14**
Handling
data 1:
Drawing bar
graphs

**HD2c/4;
2de/5**

**C/D1
O/E1
D/D
I/E3**

Content

- Interpretation and construction of bar and line (trend) graphs
- Collection, organisation and display of data
- Calculation of range and mean.

Organisation

Group discussion is required for Q1. Q6 requires a class survey to be carried out.

Introductory activity

Our school
Real data about the school's first-year intake could be used to introduce the work. Draw a bar graph from the data and emphasise the need for a title and labels for each axis.

Detailed notes

Q1	Stress that different scales can be used. Ensure pupils understand the scenario: headteacher is obtaining information for the *next* year's intake.
Graph below Q1	Title, labels and the use of a key should all be emphasised.
Q5c	A suitable scale for the vertical axis is 1 square represents 2 pupils. This will require the use of half squares.
Pupil absence table	Some pupils may have difficulty with interpretation.
Q8b	In Heinemann Mathematics 7 trend graphs were drawn using broken lines. Some discussion about the use of continuous lines may be appropriate.

Equipment

Calculator, $\frac{1}{2}$ cm squared paper, coloured pencils.

HD2ace/5

**C/E1
O/E1
D/D2
I/D1
E+**

Content

- Calculation of range
- Organisation of data in frequency tables using given class intervals
- Display of data in a frequency diagram
- Collection and display of data from practical measurements.

Organisation

The collection and organisation of data for Q4 should be planned in advance.

Detailed notes

Q1	It may be necessary to revise important points relating to class intervals:

- the lowest value is in the first class interval and the highest value is in the last class interval
- each value can only be placed in one class interval
- all class intervals are of equal size.

W14, Graph 8	For clarity the class intervals are labelled vertically on the graph.
Q1f	The meaning of '40 kg or more' may need an explanation.
Q2e	The meaning of 'shorter than 150 cm' may need an explanation.
Q3	An additional class interval, 180–189 cm, is needed for height.
Q4	These measurements could be taken group by group as pupils are working through earlier questions, and the heights and weights displayed for all to use. The class intervals given in Q1 and Q2 are likely to be suitable.

Additional activity

Pulse rates
Collect the resting pulse rate for each member of the class. Display this data in a bar graph using suitable class intervals (60–64, 65–69 . . .). Compare this with a graph of pulse rates taken after physical activity, for example, standing and sitting 20 times.

Equipment

Personal scales, 2-metre tape measure, $\frac{1}{2}$ cm squared paper.
For the Additional activity: a seconds timer.

Content

- Use of different sizes of class interval for a single set of data
- Calculation of range
- Organisation of data in a frequency table, choosing suitable class intervals
- Display of data in a frequency diagram with class intervals.

Detailed notes

Q1 Allow pupils to discuss answers in groups; then highlight the
- advantages and disadvantages of different class intervals
- optimum number of class intervals to choose (between 5 and 12).

Pupils may need help to realise that
- the size of the interval 6–10 is 5 (6, 7, 8, 9, 10)
- the size of the interval 10–20 is 11.

Listing all numbers in the interval may help.

Q3 A trial and improvement procedure could be used for choosing suitable class intervals. For a range of 29:

Trial size of interval	Number of intervals		Comment
2	29 ÷ 2	14 or 15	too many
6	29 ÷ 6	4 or 5	too few
4	29 ÷ 4	7 or 8	suitable

Equipment

None.

Content

- Meaning of discrete and continuous data
- Organisation of continuous data given/choosing suitable class intervals
- Display of continuous data as a frequency diagram with class intervals.

Class intervals use the word 'under' to help pupils place boundary measurements correctly, for example, 10·5 – under 11·0. The lower boundary is included but the upper is not.

Introductory activity

Counted or measured
Through class discussion, differentiate between discrete data 'counted' and continuous data 'measured'. Pupils should list at least 5 things that are measured: time taken to walk to school, height of church tower, weight of a packet of biscuits . . .; and 5 things that are counted: number of red cars in the car-park, number of pupils present in class, number of posters on the wall, ...

Detailed notes

Q2 The word 'under' does not appear in the graph. It may be necessary to discuss this form of labelling.

Q3 If pupils need help choosing suitable class intervals then suggest
- Javelin   52·0 – under 52·5
               52·5 – under 53·0 . . .
- 200 metres   24·5 – under 25·0
               25·0 – under 25·5 . . .

Equipment

None.

48
Handling
data 1:
Survey sheets

UA4a/5
HD2ab/5

C/E2
O/E1
D/D1
I/E1, 2
PSE
E+

Content

- Design and use of a survey sheet for the collection of class data
- Organisation, display and interpretation of data.

Pupils are required to use problem-solving skills to investigate a real-life situation.

Organisation

Pupils should work in groups to produce questionnaires. The whole class will be involved in providing data. Pupils could work individually to write about their group's findings.

Detailed notes

Panel above Q1 A class discussion would be useful to set the scene and emphasise the questions which the survey must answer.

Q3 Here is a possible way of organising the data:

Name	Sandwiches				Crisps			Fruit		Soft drink			
	ham	tuna	tomato	cheese	plain	vinegar	prawn	apple	orange	cola	orange	cherry	lemon
Joe Smith		✓		✓		✓		✓			✓		

Q4 A selection of the pupils' findings could be discussed and used for a wall display.

Q5 This challenge may be more easily attempted if data is recorded as above.

Additional activity

Lunch choices
Ask pupils to investigate the number of different possible choices of packed lunch.

Equipment

Plain paper, 2 mm, $\frac{1}{2}$ cm and 1 cm squared paper.

S17
Handling
data 1:
Bar graphs

HD2cf/5

C/D1
O/D1
D/D1
I/D1

Content

- Interpretation of bar and combined bar graphs
- Collection and organisation of data and its presentation as bar and combined bar graphs.

Organisation

For efficiency, help to collate the data for Q6, but it is important that all pupils doing this work experience data collection.

Introductory activity

Class survey
A class survey similar to Q6 may be a good way of introducing this topic. Choose a survey (such as, pupils' favourite pop groups, flavours of lemonade, etc.) involving four possible choices; collect and organise the data in a frequency table then display it in a bar graph.

Detailed notes

Q4, 5 Encourage pupils to explain orally what each graph 'shows more clearly'.

Q6 Results of this survey could be displayed in similar ways to those illustrated.

Equipment

$\frac{1}{2}$ cm or 1 cm squared paper, coloured pencils.

Content

- Interpretation and construction of bar-line and trend graphs.

Equipment

2 mm squared paper.

S18
Handling
data 1:
Bar-line and
trend graphs

HD2cf/5

D/D1
I/D1

Detailed notes

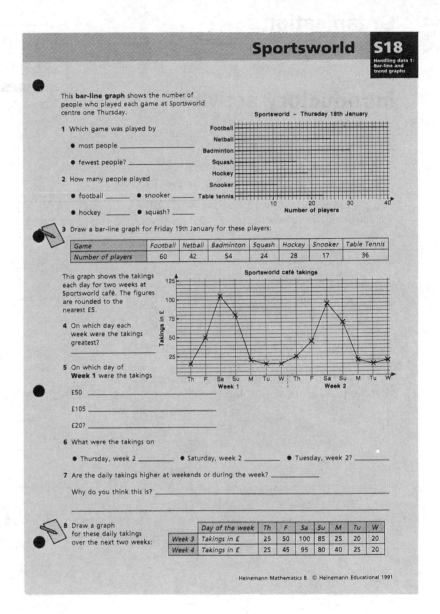

Q3 Suggest that on 2 mm squared paper the pupils use a scale of 1 small interval to represent 1 player.

Q8 If necessary suggest that on 2 mm squared paper pupils use the same scale as in Q4.

S19

Handling
data 1:
Horizontal bar
graphs

HD2acf/4

C/D1
O/D1
D/D1
I/D1
PSE

Content

- Interpretation of information in tabular form
- Organisation of data in a frequency table
- Display and interpretation of this data as a horizontal bar graph
- Collection, organisation and display of class data.

Organisation

The survey in Q5 is best carried out by a small group.

Introductory activity

Sport survey
Use the following example to ensure the pupils understand
- that each pupil surveyed had 3 votes
- how to use tally marks in a frequency table.

Ten pupils were asked to choose their top 3 sports from the following:

A – Basketball, B – Cycling, C – Gymnastics, D – Judo, E – Swimming.

Pupil	Votes	Pupil	Votes
1	D B E	6	B C E
2	A C E	7	B D E
3	B C D	8	A C E
4	A C E	9	A D E
5	A B C	10	A C E

Organise this information in a frequency table and display it as a horizontal bar graph.

Detailed notes

Q1 Pupils should score out each vote as it is transferred to the frequency table.

Q2 The bars in the graph will be horizontal.

Q5 Advice may be needed on a suitable way of collecting and recording the data.

Equipment

$\frac{1}{2}$ cm squared paper.

Content

- Interpretation of bar and combined bar graphs
- Interpretation of a line graph in trend graph form
- Interpretation of tables.

Equipment

None.

E8
E9
Handling data 1: Interpretatio of graphs

HD2f/5

O/E1
I/E1

Detailed notes

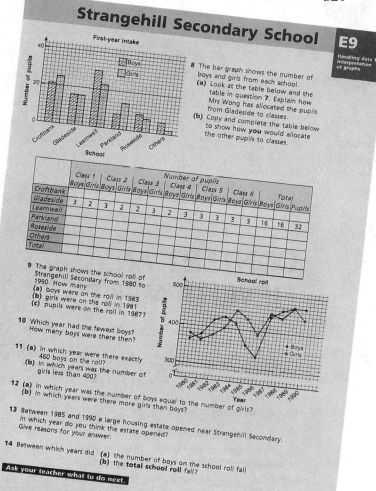

Strangehill Secondary School

E9
Handling data 1: Interpretation of graphs

8 The bar graph shows the number of boys and girls from each school.
  (a) Look at the table below and the table in question **7**. Explain how Mrs Wong has allocated the pupils from Gladeside to classes.
  (b) Copy and complete the table below to show how **you** would allocate the other pupils to classes.

	Class 1		Class 2		Class 3		Class 4		Class 5		Class 6		Total	
	Boys	Girls	Boys	Girls	Boys	Girls	Boys	Girls	Boys	Girls	Boys	Girls	Boys/Girls	Pupils
Croftbank														
Gladeside	3	2	3	2	2	3	2	3	3	3	3	3	16 16	32
Learnwell														
Parkland														
Roseside														
Others														
Total														

9 The graph shows the school roll of Strangehill Secondary from 1980 to 1990. How many
  (a) boys were on the roll in 1983
  (b) girls were on the roll in 1981
  (c) pupils were on the roll in 1987?

10 Which year had the fewest boys? How many boys were there then?

11 (a) In which year were there exactly 460 boys on the roll?
   (b) In which years was the number of girls less than 400?

12 (a) In which year was the number of boys equal to the number of girls?
   (b) In which years were there more girls than boys?

13 Between 1985 and 1990 a large housing estate opened near Strangehill Secondary. In which year do you think the estate opened? Give reasons for your answer.

14 Between which years did (a) the number of boys on the school roll fall
                            (b) the **total school roll** fall?

Ask your teacher what to do next.

E8 Strangehill Secondary School

ling data 1: erpretation of graphs

Pupils from five local primary schools go to Strangehill Secondary. Mrs Wong, the headmistress, drew this bar graph to show the number of first-year pupils from each school.

1 From what school did
  (a) most (b) fewest pupils come?

2 (a) How many more pupils came from Croftbank than from Gladeside?
  (b) Did more or fewer pupils come from Learnwell than from Parkland and Roseside together? How many more or fewer?

3 (a) How many pupils in total came from the five schools?
  (b) Strangehill had a first-year roll of 177. Give possible reasons why the number is different from your answer to part (a).

Pupil distribution

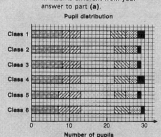

There are six classes in the first year. The graph shows the distribution of pupils in each class.

4 Which classes have
  (a) eight pupils from Croftbank
  (b) only three pupils from Parkland
  (c) more than five pupils from Gladeside?

5 What does the ■ shading show?

6 What do you notice about the way Mrs Wong has distributed the pupils?

7 Copy and complete the table.

	Number of pupils						
	Class						
	1	2	3	4	5	6	Total
Croftbank							
Gladeside	5	5	5	5	6	6	32
Learnwell							
Parkland							
Roseside							
Others							
Total		29					

Q8a Some pupils may need guidance about what to write. They should realise that the number of boys/girls may change but not the total number of pupils.

Q8b If necessary reproduce this complex table for the pupils who should be guided to complete the total columns first.

Q9 Some pupils may be unfamiliar with the use of a broken scale, as in the vertical axis.

Q3b A possible reason might be incomers to the district.

Q4 Pupils need to appreciate that the shading in the pupil distribution graph relates to the *first-year intake*.

Q6 If necessary discuss the distribution of Gladeside pupils.

Q12a There should be some discussion about intermediate points having no meaning.

Q14 Encourage pupils to look at the gradient of the graph rather than calculate actual roll sizes.

45

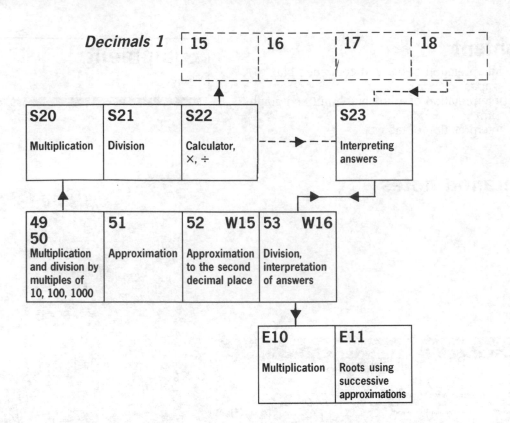

Decimals 1

| 15 | 16 | 17 | 18 |

S20	**S21**	**S22**
Multiplication	Division	Calculator, ×, ÷

S23
Interpreting answers

49 50	**51**	**52 W15**	**53 W16**
Multiplication and division by multiples of 10, 100, 1000	Approximation	Approximation to the second decimal place	Division, interpretation of answers

E10	**E11**
Multiplication	Roots using successive approximations

CONTENT AND DEVELOPMENT

Core

Heinemann Mathematics 8, *Decimals 1* provides consolidation and development of the work on place value to three decimal places and on addition, subtraction, multiplication and division to two decimal places.

Decimals 2 provides consolidation and development of the work on multiplication by multiples of 10, 100; approximation, division by calculator and interpretation of calculator answers as well as providing the introduction to

- multiplication by multiples of 1000
- division by multiples of 10, 100, 1000
- approximation to the second decimal place.

Support

S20–S22 provide lead-in material to *Decimals 1* (Core Textbook pages 15 to 18). Thereafter pupils can either go to S23 and finish or go to Core Textbook page 49. S23 provides parallel work to Core Textbook page 53.

Extension

E10 and E11 may be attempted at any point after completion of Core Textbook page 50. E10 covers the multiplication of two one-place decimals and E11 involves finding square and cube roots by successive approximations.

A calculator should be used throughout.

National Curriculum (England and Wales)

UA2b
N2ab, 3cf, 4abd
SM4ac

Mathematics 5–14 (Scotland)

RTN/D4   RTN/E3
MD/D2, 3, 4   MD/E2, 4
RN/D1   RN/E1
PS/E1
FE/E4
ME/D9   ME/E5
PFS/E1
PSE
E+

EQUIPMENT

Calculator, 1 cm squared paper, ruler, worksheet of blank number lines.

For the Introductory activities: leaflets advertising the products of a garden centre, 1 cm cubes.

Content

- Multiplication and division of decimals by multiples of 10, 100 and 1000
- Products and quotients involving up to three place decimals.
  Written methods are used in examples involving money, measures and averages.

Organisation

Each Introductory activity should be taught separately and then followed by the appropriate questions. Introductory activity 3 sets the scene for Core Textbook page 50.

Introductory activities

Leaflets from garden centres could be discussed to help set the scenario of the market garden.

1 Multiplication by 10, 100 and 1000
The effect of multiplication by 10, 100 and 1000 with digits moving left should be shown by first considering the whole number case then the decimal, for example:

Detailed notes

49
50
Decimals 2:
Multiplicatio
and division
by multiples
10, 100, 1000

N2ab,
3c/5

RTN/E3
MD/E2
ME/E5

- plants cost 7p each or £0·07, so
  10 cost 7 × 10 = 70p or
  £0·07 × 10 = £0·70
  digits move 1 place left

  100 cost 7 × 100 = 700p or
  £0·07 × 100 = £7·00
  digits move 2 places left

  1000 cost 7 × 1000 = 7000p or
  £0·07 × 1000 = £70·00
  digits move 3 places left
- Repeat for heathers costing 70p each or £0·70.

2 Multiplication by multiples of 10, 100 and 1000
This should be dealt with as indicated in the panel above Q3 on Core Textbook page 49.

3 Division by 10, 100, 1000 and multiples of these
Division should be treated in a similar way to multiplication but emphasising the digit shift to the right.

Equipment

For the Introductory activities: leaflets advertising the products of a garden centre.

49. Q2 Stress that the price must be in pounds to ensure answers in decimal form.

49. Q4 This use of average may need to be explained.

50. Q3 Pupils may have to be reminded about calculating an average.

50, Q4, Q5 Some pupils may misinterpret and calculate the average daily total.

50, Q6 Some explanation of 'area of ground in m² per plant' may be required.

51
Decimals 2:
pproximation

N2a,3f/5

MD/E4
RN/D1
RN/E1

Content

- Division of whole numbers and one-place decimals by one- and two-digit whole numbers, using a calculator
- Calculation of mean
- Rounding to the nearest whole number and to the first decimal place.

Introductory activity

The scenario of a fruit farm like Sandydale should be discussed. Pupils who have visited a fruit farm or who have worked at berry picking should be able to contribute to the discussion.

Approximation to the nearest whole number and to the first decimal place
Revise interpretation of a calculator display to the nearest whole number and to the first decimal place using the methods illustrated in the panels. Some possible examples which result in different displays are:

$1050 \div 36$ $592 \cdot 6 \div 25$ $103 \div 42$ $34 \cdot 7 \div 48$

Make pupils aware of different terminology which can be used when rounding:
- to the nearest whole number or to the nearest unit
- to the first decimal place or to one decimal place or to the nearest tenth.

Detailed notes

Q3c Stress that *each person's* mean weight of fruit picked per day is required.

Equipment

Calculator.
A sheet of blank number lines may assist pupils when rounding numbers:

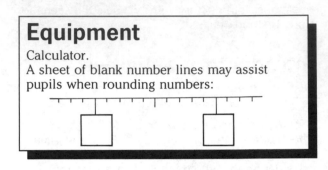

52
W15
(Q1)
Decimals 2:
pproximation
o the second
ecimal place

UA2b/5
N2a, 3f,
4a/5

MD/E4
E+

Content

- Division of whole numbers, one- and two-place decimals by two-digit whole numbers, using a calculator
- Calculation of mean weight, volume and area
- Rounding to the second decimal place.

Introductory activity

Approximation to the second decimal place
The panel shows the method of rounding to the second decimal place. Some possible examples which result in different displays are:

$46 \cdot 2 \div 25$ $45 \cdot 6 \div 18$ $39 \div 33$
$5 \cdot 6 \div 12$ $354 \div 42$

Make pupils aware of different terminology which can be used when rounding to the second decimal place or to two decimal places or to the nearest hundredth.

Detailed notes

Q4b Stress that the units required are *grams* per square metre.

Q5 Difficulty with interpretation is anticipated, so draw attention to the units in which each answer has to be expressed. Pupils' answers should be discussed, particularly to Q5(b) where the average is $11 \cdot 875$ and therefore the approximation can be either $11 \cdot 87$ or $11 \cdot 88$.

Additional activity

The following highlight some difficulties:

	Display	Rounding
$71 \cdot 4 \div 67$ =	$1 \cdot 0656716$	$\longrightarrow 1 \cdot 07$
$99 \cdot 9 \div 99$ =	$1 \cdot 0090909$	$\longrightarrow 1 \cdot 01$
$1111 \div 200$ =	$5 \cdot 555$	$\longrightarrow 5 \cdot 55$ or $5 \cdot 56$
$112 \div 51$ =	$2 \cdot 1960784$	$\longrightarrow 2 \cdot 20$
$56 \cdot 1 \div 56$ =	$1 \cdot 0017857$	$\longrightarrow 1 \cdot 00$
$73 \cdot 9 \div 74$ =	$0 \cdot 9986486$	$\longrightarrow 1 \cdot 00$

Equipment

Calculator.
A sheet of blank number lines may assist pupils when rounding numbers.

53
W16
Decimals 2:
Division,
Interpretatio
of answers

N2b,3c,
4a/5; 4d/
5 → 6

MD/D4
RN/D1
PS/E1

Content

- Division of a whole number by a two-digit whole number resulting in a decimal display
- Interpretation of a decimal calculator display in context
- Calculation of exact remainders
- Recognition of square numbers.

Organisation

Class discussion on Q1 to Q3 before proceeding to the Introductory activity.

Introductory activity

Finding the remainder
This may be done in a practical way where the pupils can see a 'model' of a division using cubes.

26 cubes placed in stacks of four

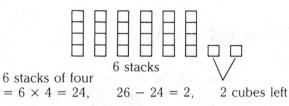

6 stacks of four
$= 6 \times 4 = 24$, $26 - 24 = 2$,   2 cubes left

$26 \div 4 = 6 \cdot 5$

26 cubes placed in stacks of seven

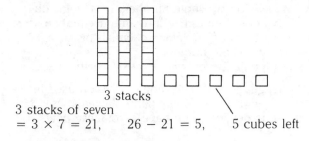

3 stacks of seven
$= 3 \times 7 = 21$, $26 - 21 = 5$,   5 cubes left

$26 \div 7 = 3 \cdot 7142857$

Detailed notes

Q1   Pupils should realise that the exact value of the decimal part is not important. The context determines whether to round up or down.

Panel above Q4   This scenario should be discussed following on from the Introductory activity.

W16, Q1   Check pupils answers before they proceed to Q2.

Equipment

Calculator.
For the Introductory activity: 1 cm cubes.

S20
Decimals 2:
Multiplication

N3e/4 → 5
SM4a/5

RTN/D4
MD/D2, 3
ME/D9

Content

- Multiplication of one- and two-place decimals by a single-digit whole number, 10 and 100
- Conversion from Imperial to metric units.

Introductory activity

Metric/Imperial units
Discuss metric and Imperial units of different measures, in particular, feet/metres, miles/kilometres, pints/litres, since these occur on the page; but yards/metres, gallons/litres, pounds/kilograms, ounces/grams and so on may also arise in the discussion.

Detailed notes

Q1   These familiar heights shown in the illustrations should help reinforce the approximate foot/metre relationship.

Q1, 2, 3   The following approximate relationships could be memorised by pupils:

10 feet ———→ 3 metres
5 miles ———→ 8 kilometres
1 pint ———→ $\frac{1}{2}$ litre

Equipment

None.

S21
Decimals 2:
Division

N3c/4 → 5
SM4c/7

RTN/D4
MD/D3
ME/D9

Content

- Division of whole numbers by a single-digit whole number resulting in a decimal answer
- Division of one-place decimals by a single-digit whole number
- Calculation of average cost, length, speed.

The language and recording of division used in earlier years of the Heinemann Mathematics course is described on page T2 of these notes.

Introductory activity

Motoring holiday
Discuss the scenario of a motoring holiday. Each question on the page has a worked example and time should be taken to ensure that the pupils understand these fully. Particular attention should be paid to the interpretation of the tables. Emphasise that there are five different sized groups of people each on a different holiday.

Detailed notes

Q3 The calculations for Lisa should be done mentally.

Equipment

None.

S22
Decimals 2:
Calculator
×, ÷

N3c, 4a/5

RTN/D4
MD/D4
PSE

Content

- Interpretation of written and tabular information
- Multiplication and division of one- and two-place decimals by one- and two-digit whole numbers using a calculator
- Calculator division of whole numbers by two- and three-digit whole numbers resulting in decimal answers.

The use of a calculator allows pupils to concentrate on interpretation of information.

Introductory activity

Sponsored jog
The scenario of a sponsored jog should be discussed. The method of finding by multiplication the total distance run should be established. Use a lap of, say, 2 km and ask for distance covered in 3 laps, 4 laps and so on.

Detailed notes

Q3 It may be easier to complete the 'distance' column first, rather than complete a row at a time. Some help may be required to complete the last two rows.

Q4 Before this question is tackled, ask pupils to find their own normal walking 'stride length' by counting 10 paces, measuring the distance and calculating the average stride length.

Q5 table Some help may be required to complete the last two rows.

Equipment

Calculator.

S23
Decimals 2:
Interpreting
answers

N3c, 4a/5

MD/D4
RN/D1
PSE

Content

- Interpretation of written and tabular information
- Division of a whole number by one- and two-digit whole numbers resulting in a decimal display
- Interpretation of a decimal calculator display in context
- Calculation of exact remainders.

Introductory activity

See Introductory activity for Core Textbook page 53, *Finding the remainder*.

Detailed notes

Q1 Some pupils may use multiplication or repeated addition, neither of which should be discouraged.

Q2 Due to the size of the numbers pupils will be forced to divide. Some help may be required at first to interpret the answers.

Q2, 3 There may be difficulty in selecting the appropriate information from the cartons.

Equipment

Calculator.

Content

- Multiplication by calculator of two one-place decimals
- Investigation of the maximum area of fixed-perimeter rectangles
- Generalisation to predict the pair of numbers with the greatest product when only their sum is known.

Introductory activity

Multiplication by calculator of two one-place decimals

The result of multiplying two one-place decimals can be illustrated by examples such as the following:

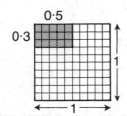

The area of the shaded rectangle

- by counting squares, is $\frac{15}{100} = 0.15$ of the unit square.
- using the formula $A = lb$, is 0.5×0.3
  Thus $0.5 \times 0.3 = 0.15$
  Compare the position of the decimal point in these examples.
  $5 \times 3 = 15$, $5 \times 0.3 = 1.5$,
  $0.5 \times 3 = 1.5$, $0.5 \times 0.3 = 0.15$

Detailed notes

E10
Decimals 2: Multiplication

N4a/7

RTN/E3
MD/E4
FE/E4
PFS/E1
PSE

Q1a Each rectangle should be drawn in both 'landscape' orientation.

and 'portrait' orientation.

Q2 Note the gradual change in language from 'area of a rectangle' to the non-contextual 'product of two decimals'.

Q3, 4 The pupils are expected to complete tables like the one in Q2.

Q5 A concise explanation might be: 'Each number in the pair is equal to half the known sum.' Encourage pupils to express their own conclusions as concisely as possible both in writing and orally.

Equipment

Calculator, 1 cm squared paper, ruler.

Content

- Use of trial and improvement methods
- Finding square and cube roots by successive approximation.

Detailed notes

Panel below Q1 'Try 2·5', because it is half way between 2 and 3. 'Try 2·65', because it is half way between 2·6 and 2·7.

Q2 Some help in identifying the initial estimate may be required. Check answers by calculating the area.

Q3b The original area is halved, half of 256 cm^2.

Q5 Some help in identifying the initial estimate may be required. Check answers by calculating the volume.

Equipment

Calculator.

55	56 W17	57	58 W17
Language and recording	Measuring and drawing	Directions and bearings	Bearings

CONTENT AND DEVELOPMENT

Core

Heinemann Mathematics 7 revises right, acute, obtuse and reflex angles, introduces straight angle and angle sum of a triangle, and includes three-figure bearings, estimating, measuring and drawing angles using a circular protractor.

Heinemann Mathematics 8, *Angles 1*, revises and consolidates some of this work and also covers:

- naming angles and shapes using letters
- measuring and drawing angles using 180° and 360° protractors.

Angles 2 in *Part 4*, deals with additional work on bearings and includes angle properties associated with intersecting and parallel lines and triangles.

National Curriculum (England and Wales)

UA3ad
SM2abdf

Mathematics 5–14 (Scotland)

RS/D1
PM/D2   **PM/E1**
A/D2   **A/E**
PSE

RELATED ACTIVITIES

1 Map-reading
Maps and compasses could be used to form the basis of a class discussion on navigation, hill-walking, orienteering or similar activities in which finding direction is important. The discussion should focus on how direction can be measured and recorded using compass points and bearings.

2 Logo
The use of Logo on a computer allows pupils to use commands involving distance and turning right and left through a specified number of degrees. Work of this nature can be used to reinforce the concept of angle as an amount of turning.

EQUIPMENT

Ruler, 360° protractor, 180° protractor.

For an Introductory activity: compass, map.

Content

- Naming vertices, arms, angles and shapes using letters
- Acute, obtuse, right and straight angles.

Introductory activity

Naming angles
Emphasise that an angle is formed when two straight lines (arms) meet at a point (vertex). Discuss arms and vertices of angles made by hands of a clock, legs of a folding table, sloping roofs and so on.

There should also be some discussion of an angle as a rotation, and examples could include blackboard compasses or the hands of a clock and so on.

Stress that
- 1 letter is used to name a vertex
- 2 letters are used to name an arm
- 3 letters are used to name an angle.

A diagram similar to the one in Q6 could be used to illustrate why three letters are necessary.

Detailed notes

Q4 Emphasise the difference between the *name* (ABC) and the *type* (acute) of angle.

Q7 Ensure pupils name different angles rather than give different names for the same angle.

Additional activity

Naming angles
A large diagram such as the one below could be displayed and pupils could be asked to
- point to angles named by the teacher
- name angles pointed to by the teacher.

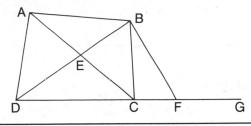

Equipment

None.

Content

- Estimation of angle
- Measurement and drawing of angles to the nearest degree
- Following flowchart instructions for using a semi-circular protractor.

Introductory activity

Making angles
Ask pupils to estimate and sketch angles of around 90°, 50°, 30°, 140°, 180° and so on. The angles should then be labelled acute, obtuse, right or straight as appropriate.

Detailed notes

Q2 It may be necessary to demonstrate the use of a protractor.

Q3 Pupils should use their estimates to ensure that they are reading the correct scale.

W17, Q1 Insist that the pupils estimate each angle before measuring. Rotating the page may help.

Q5 In the flow chart instructions it may be necessary to increase the length of BC so that it extends beyond the protractor.

Q7a The phrase 'common arm' may need some explanation.

Q7b Note that there are two possible solutions: 29° and 99°.

Additional activity

Drawing a rhombus
Challenge the pupils to draw a rhombus ABCD with
- side AB equal to 8 cm
- angle ABC equal to 65°
- angle BCD equal to 115°.

Equipment

180° protractor.

Content

- The eight main compass points and their three-figure bearing equivalents
- Use of bearings (multiples of 45°).

Introductory activity

Compass bearings
With the aid of a compass and map, revise the positions of the main compass points. These could be drawn on the floor and a pupil could stand in the centre with outstretched arm to demonstrate turning clockwise and anticlockwise to point to N, S, NW, SE and so on.

Discuss the bearing of the Sun (South) and the direction of shadows (North) at 12 noon GMT in Britain.

Detailed notes

Q2d There are two possible answers.

Q3 Since two positions are given, take care to identify the correct starting position from which the bearing is taken.

Q8e There are two possible answers.

Q8f There are three possible answers.

Equipment

For the Introductory activity: compass, map.

58
W17
(Q3)

Angles 1: Bearings

SM2ad/5

PM/E1
A/D2
A/E
PSE

Content

- Measurement and calculation of bearings in given diagrams
- Measurement and calculation of distances and bearings in scale drawings
- Interpretation of information in written and visual form.

Detailed notes

Q1 It may be necessary to demonstrate how to measure a bearing.

Q3 This involves the use of scale and measurement of distance and direction.

Q4 Pupils could be asked to devise a quick way of finding back-bearings (adding or subtracting 180°) but it is not intended that this method be taught formally.

If a 180° protractor is being used, the 'back-bearings' cannot be measured directly and some calculation is necessary.

Additional activity

Treasure hunt
Ask more able pupils to devise games involving drawing their own map to a fixed scale and describing a route using bearings and distances for others to follow to find hidden treasure.

Equipment

Ruler, 360° protractor.

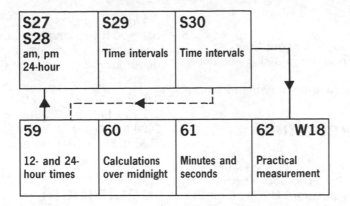

CONTENT AND DEVELOPMENT

Core

Heinemann Mathematics 7 covers work on writing dates, 24-hour time and time durations.

Heinemann Mathematics 8 revises and consolidates:

- am, pm, 12-hour and 24-hour notations
- interpretation of timetables
- time calculations using addition and subtraction
- measuring time to the nearest second.

Support

S27–S30 can be used as parallel work to that of the Core. On completion pupils should attempt the practical work on Core Textbook page 62. It can also be used as lead-in material to Core Textbook page 59.

National Curriculum (England & Wales)

SM4a

Mathematics 5–14 (Scotland)

PSE
RTN/D4
AS/E2
T/C1, 2, 4   T/D1, 2, 3   T/E1

EQUIPMENT

Stopwatch.

For the Introductory activities: newspaper or magazine showing television schedules.

59
Time:
12- and 24-
hour times

SM4a/4

PSE
T/D1, 2

Content

- Conversion of 12-hour to 24-hour times
- Time calculations, h and min, using addition and subtraction
- Interpretation of information in written form.

Introductory activities

1 TV schedules
Radio Times, TV Times or newspapers could be brought in by pupils for discussion. Are they detailed in 12- or 24-hour notation? How can one distinguish between a morning and an evening programme in both instances? What if the 12-hour notation does not include the abbreviations am and pm?

2 Video recorders
Ask about the length of tapes available, in hours and minutes. A mental method of calculating the duration of a programme could be revised, for example:

'Life's a Laugh'   1325 to 1410
1325 to 1400 is 35 minutes
1400 to 1410 is 10 minutes
That is 35 + 10 = 45 minutes altogether.

Equipment

For Introductory activity 1: newspaper or magazine showing television schedules.

Detailed notes

Telly viewing panels above Q1	Some help with interpretation may be required. Certain titles will provide helpful clues, for example, 'Lunchtime News'
Time line above Q1	This can be used for either time conversions or calculations.
Q2a	No formal written method is expected.
Q2b	Modern technology allows a 3-hour tape to record for 6 hours using a slow-speed facility. The question assumes recording is at normal speed.

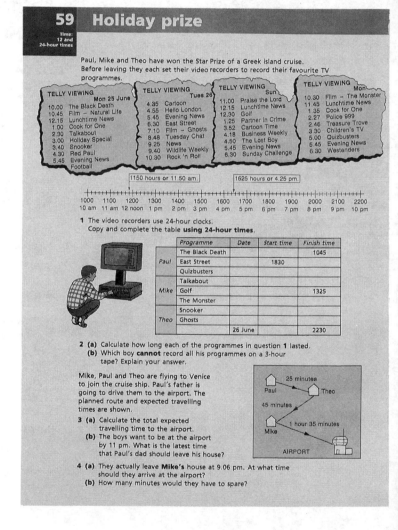

Content

- Conversion of 24-hour to 12-hour times
- Interpretation of information from timetables
- Time calculations, h and min, including over midnight, using addition and subtraction.

Introductory activity

Timetables
Pupils could obtain timetables and find out that 12 midnight may be recorded as 0000 hours. Pupils should write arrival and departure times in the three ways illustrated. Examples using addition techniques should be given by providing departure times and lengths of journeys and then asking pupils to find the arrival times.

Mental calculation is expected. For example:

A train leaves London at 2340 and takes $6\frac{1}{2}$ hours to reach Glasgow.

2340 and 6 hours is 0540,
0540 and 30 minutes is 0610
OR
2340 and 30 minutes is 0010,
0010 and 6 hours is 0610

Detailed notes

60
Time:
Calculations
over midnight

SM4a/4

PSE
T/D1, 2

Time line below Q2	This can be used for either time conversions or calculations.
Q2	No formal written method is expected.
Cruise time-table beside Q3–5	Some help with interpretation of the timetable may be required.

Equipment
None.

Content

- Changing seconds to minutes and seconds
- Time calculations, seconds to two decimal places, using addition.

Introductory activity

Four by 400 m relay
The following example illustrates the method for time conversions from seconds to minutes and seconds.

Lap 1	52·06 s	1 minute	=	60 s
Lap 2	49·76 s	2 minutes	=	120 s
Lap 3	49·98 s	3 minutes	=	180 s
Lap 4	50·34 s	4 minutes	=	240 s
Total	202·14 s			

So 202·14 s lies between 3 and 4 minutes.
202·14 − 180 = 22·14 so 202·14 s = 3 min 22·14 s

The use of calculators is inappropriate.

Detailed notes

61
Time:
Minutes and
seconds

SM4a/4

RTN/D4
AS/E2
T/E1

| Panel above Q3 | Times are now measured in seconds to two decimal places. Stress that 54·89 s does not mean 54 minutes 89 seconds. When converting seconds to minutes and seconds pupils may be helped by working with the whole number of seconds first, then adding the decimal part. |

Equipment
None.

**62
W18**

Time:
Practical
measurement

SM4a/4

T/D3

Content

- Measurement of time
- Time calculations, whole number of seconds, using addition
- Conversion of seconds to minutes and seconds.

Organisation

Pupils work in pairs alternating the role of timer between tasks.

Pupil A times pupil B for the tasks described in Section 1.
Pupil B records these times in his/her own workbook.

Pupil B times pupil A for the tasks described in Section 2.
Pupil A records these times in his/her own workbook.

Introductory activity

Using a stopwatch
Pupils should practise using the stopwatches to time each other for some simple activities, for example putting 10 counters in a pile or standing up and sitting down 20 times.

Additional activities

1 Class results
Calculate average times for (a) each task and (b) each section and discuss their relative difficulties. Find the fastest pupil for each task and section.

2 Class pentathlon
Teams of five pupils could design five simple timed events. Other teams complete the timed events and the lowest total time wins the pentathlon.

Equipment

A stopwatch for each pair of pupils.
Most digital watches offer a stopwatch facility accurate to 0·01 s.

**S27
S28**

Time:
am, pm
24-hour

2/3e4

**T/C1, 2, 4
T/D1**

Content

- Interpretation of information in written form
- am and pm notation
- Conversion of 12-hour to 24-hour times.

Introductory activity

TV schedules
See the notes on Introductory activity 1 for Core Textbook page 59.

Detailed notes

S27, Q2b	The use of 'A' to mean am may need explanation.
S28, illustration above Q2	Discuss playing times of video tapes and their time codes.
S28, Q4b	Note that the time goes over midnight to Tuesday 28th.

Equipment

Digital watch.
For the Introductory activity: newspaper or magazine showing television schedules.

Content

- Time calculations, min, h and min, using addition and subtraction
- Ordering 12-hour times.

Detailed notes

Time line Q1 Some explanation may be required about how to use the time line.

Time line Q2 Ensure that pupils realise that the time line is marked at 5-minute intervals.

Equipment

None.

Content

- Time calculations, min, h and min, using addition and subtraction.
Both 12-hour and 24-hour notations are used.

Introductory activity

Some preliminary discussion may be required to set the scene. Emphasise the correct time of the meeting and the early and late arrival times.

Detailed notes

Q2 Several different methods might be used to calculate time intervals. As in the Core Textbook pages, mental methods should be encouraged.

Equipment

None.

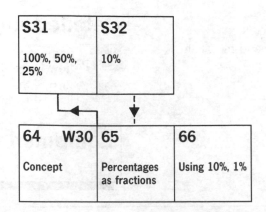

S31	S32
100%, 50%, 25%	10%

64 W30	65	66
Concept	Percentages as fractions	Using 10%, 1%

CONTENT AND DEVELOPMENT

Core

Heinemann Mathematics 7 covers work on the meaning of per cent, fractions of 100 as percentages, calculations based on 10% and percentage calculations based on decimal fractions.

Heinemann Mathematics 8 revises and develops these ideas and covers:

- concept of per cent, including 100%
- common percentages expressed as fractions
- calculation of a percentage using the fractional equivalent
- calculations based on 10% and 1%.

Percentages 2 in *Part 4* covers use of the calculator, percentage increase and decrease and changing fractions to percentages.

Support

All pupils should attempt Core Textbook page 64. Those who have difficulty with subsequent work should be directed to Support pages S31 and S32 which provide parallel work to that of Core Textbook pages 65 and 66.

It may be valuable for some pupils to attempt the Core Textbook pages on completion of Support material.

National Curriculum (England and Wales)

N2b, 3d

Mathematics 5–14 (Scotland)

D/E2
RTN/D4
FPR/D1   FPR/E3

RELATED ACTIVITIES

Percentages in use
Percentages are in evidence all around us. Ask pupils to collect examples of percentages from as many different sources as possible, for example newspapers, magazines, adverts and leaflets. These should be displayed and used as the basis for class discussion and problems. Teachers may need to provide some suitable examples.

Percentages are also used in other subject areas and pupils can be encouraged to look for applications of percentages in other curriculum areas. These too may be incorporated into class work.

EQUIPMENT

Coloured pencils, dictionary.

Content

- Concept of per cent, including 100%
- A fraction of the form $\frac{x}{100}$ expressed as a percentage
- Construction of percentage pie charts.

Organisation

Group or class discussion of Q4 may increase the length of the list. However, it may be advisable to have some examples prepared in advance.

Detailed notes

64
W30
Percentages
Concept

N2b/5

D/E2
RTN/D4

Q1 — This activity could be continued throughout the section.

W30, Q1 — Pupils should compare designs and realise that many different designs are possible.

W30, Q4 — Some pupils may need guidance about where to draw the starting line in the pie chart.

Q4 — A dictionary could be made available. In some words 'cent' does not mean 100, for example, 'decent'.

Equipment

Coloured pencils, dictionary.

Content

- Changing percentages to vulgar fractions
- Calculation of a percentage of a quantity by using the vulgar fraction equivalent.

Pupils should know the fractional forms of 50%, 25%, 75%, 10%, 20% and 1%.

Introductory activity

Simplifying fractions
Pupils should be reminded about the method of simplifying fractions shown on Core Textbook page 42.

Detailed notes

65
Percentages 1
Percentages
as fractions

N2b, 3d/5

RTN/D4
FPR/E3

Panel above Q3 — This is the first time that $33\frac{1}{3}\%$ has been used.

Additional activities

Ask pupils to find
- the percentage of water in Percy's Patent Hair Restorer
- the percentage of fine sand in each jar of Percy's aches and pains potion.

Equipment

None.

Content

- Calculation of 10% then multiples of 10% of a quantity
- Calculation of 1% then multiples of 1% of a quantity.

Introductory activities

1 Ten per cent and multiples
Ask pupils to discuss how to find a 40% deposit for a pair of training shoes costing £48. Discuss the various suggestions.

10% of £48 $= \frac{1}{10}$ of £48 $=$ £4·80
40% of £48 $= 4 \times 10\%$ of £48
$\qquad\qquad\quad = 4 \times$ £4·80
$\qquad\qquad\quad =$ £19·20

2 One per cent and multiples
Repeat this process to find 8% commission on sales totalling £256.

Detailed notes

Panel above Q1 — Some pupils may need to be reminded about the meaning of 'deposit'.

Q2 — Some pupils may revert to fractional equivalents. They could be asked also to use the multiples method.

Panel above Q4 — The meaning of 'commission' may need explanation.

Q6d — Some pupils may use the fact that $5\% = \frac{1}{2}$ of 10%.

Equipment

None.

S31
ercentages 1:
0%, 50%, 25%

N2b/4;
3c/5

RTN/D4
FPR/D1

Content

- Concept of per cent, including 100%
- Calculation of percentages of quantities using simple percentage/fraction equivalents, 50% and $\frac{1}{2}$, 25% and $\frac{1}{4}$
- Application of this to percentage decrease.

Detailed notes

Panel above Q1 Discuss the content of this panel. The use of actual labels and cuttings from newspapers and magazines may help set the scene.

Q1 Pupils may need to be reminded that the percentages on each label total 100.

Q3 Some pupils may need to be reminded that the whole class is 100%.

Q4 Some discussion of the terms 'save' and 'off' and how to calculate the final price may be useful.

Equipment

Red and blue coloured pencils.

S32
ercentages 1:
10%

N2b/4;
3c/5

RTN/D4
FPR/D1

Content

- Calculation of percentages of quantities using simple percentage/fraction equivalents, 10% and $\frac{1}{10}$.
- Application of this to percentage decrease
- Interpretation of information in visual form.

Introductory activities

1 Ten per cent of 100
The concept of 10% could be revised by shading 10% in different shapes such as a 10 × 10 square. The equivalence of 10%, $\frac{10}{100}$ and $\frac{1}{10}$ should be emphasised.

2 Shading 10%
Ask pupils to shade 10% of for example a 4 × 15 rectangle. This should lead to discussion about how to find 10% of 60 as $\frac{1}{10}$ of 60 = 60 ÷ 10 = 6. This should be repeated for other shapes and multiples of 10. Encourage pupils to be inventive in their shading and produce attractive patterns. A wall display could result.

3 Ten per cent in action
Ask pupils to think of examples from real life where they have seen 10% used. Collect examples and display, or draw attention to examples from the class collage. These examples could be used to set problems in context to be solved mentally, for example:
10% off in a sale, jeans £30 saving £3
10% pay rise, Paul's pay was £140 goes up £14
10% of employees made redundant, 520 employees means 52 affected
10% more in this packet, was 80 g now increased by 8 g
10% deposit to buy video, 10% of £430 = £43.

Detailed notes

Q2 Some pupils may need an explanation of the terms 'deposit' and 'marked price'.

Q3 Calculations should be done mentally.

Q4 Some pupils may find 20% as $\frac{1}{5}$. Others may find 20% as 2 × 10%.

Equipment

None.

CONTENT AND DEVELOPMENT

Core

In Heinemann Mathematics 8 *Part 1*, pupils met the terms equilateral, isosceles and scalene triangles, acute, right and obtuse angles. In *Part 2 Angles* they have covered labelling angles, measuring and drawing angles to the nearest one degree.

This section deals with:

- the use of drawing instruments to construct triangles
- the construction of composite shapes involving triangle, rectangle and square.

An investigative approach involving problem solving processes is required for elements of the work.

National Curriculum (England and Wales)

SM2bd

Mathematics 5–14 (Scotland)

PSE
PFS/E3
RS/E5, 6
A/E

RELATED ACTIVITIES

Using protractors and compasses
Although pupils may have worked fairly recently on drawing angles, some further practice in the use of protractors would be worthwhile. Practice in the use of compasses might also be necessary and drawing patterns with intersecting circles could be an interesting and worthwhile exercise.

EQUIPMENT

Plain paper, ruler, compasses, protractor, tracing paper.

67
68

onstructions:
Drawing
triangles
nd composite
shapes

SM2bd/5

PSE
PFS/E3
RS/E5, 6
A/E

Content

- Construction of triangles given three different types of information
- Construction of rectangle, square and composite shapes
- Interpretation of information presented in written and visual form and selection of materials
- Construction of accurate plans using a scale of 1 cm to 1 m.

Detailed notes

67, Garden plan above Q1 A very simple scale has been used to allow pupils to concentrate on the techniques of constructing triangles.

67, Q3 This is a challenge for pupils to adapt methods used in Q1 and Q2 to the third type of information. Some pupils may need guidance.

68, Q4 Some pupils may need help, particularly with part (d).

Additional activity

Constructing triangles
Ask pupils to investigate the three different sets of minimum information required to define triangles precisely.

The three sets of information on these pages are:

given 3 sides
given 2 sides and the included angle
given 1 side and 2 angles.

Equipment

Plain paper, ruler, compasses, protractor.

69

onstructions:
Shapes to
scale

SM2bd/5

PSE
PFS/E3
RS/E5, 6
A/E

Content

- Interpretation of information presented in written and visual form
- Construction of an accurate plan based on triangles, rectangles and squares.

Organisation

The problems of finding the dimensions from the information given could be discussed in small groups. Thereafter pupils should work individually.

Detailed notes

Q1 It may be advisable for pupils to copy the rough plan larger than it appears beside Q1, to allow lengths to be inserted clearly. Emphasise that all the information required is given on the page.

Equipment

Plain paper, ruler, protractor, tracing paper.

70	71	72	73
Number machines	Construction Evaluation	Symbolic form	Construction Evaluation

E14	E15	E16
Using a formula	Finding a formula	Construction

CONTENT AND DEVELOPMENT

Core

In Heinemann Mathematics 8, *Part 1, Word formulae*, the relationship between two quantities is described using word formulae, following recognition of patterns in tables of number pairs.

In Heinemann Mathematics 8, *Formulae*, the use of symbols is introduced and covers:

- use of one- and two-stage number machines
- construction and use of formulae
- use of shortened algebraic form for multiplication.

Extension

E14–E16 should be tackled on completion of the Core Textbook pages and involves the construction and use of more complex formulae.

National Curriculum (England and Wales)

UA2c
A3ab

Mathematics 5–14 (Scotland)

PSE
I/E1
FE/E1, 3, 4
PFS/D1

RELATED ACTIVITIES

Formulae poster
Ask pupils for examples of formulae they have used in other subjects such as Science or Home Economics. These formulae could then be displayed.

EQUIPMENT

None.

Content

- Use of one- and two-stage number machines.

Introductory activity

Factory machines

A class discussion of factory machines which repeatedly carry out the same operation, for example, a machine which puts tops on bottles, may be helpful. The words 'input' and 'output' should be mentioned. In the example above, the input is the open bottle and the output is the topped bottle.

Detailed notes

Q2 Although mentioned in the question, the use of a calculator should be unnecessary for most pupils.

Q4 Encourage more able pupils to find as many possibilities as they can.

Equipment

None.

Content

- Use of number machines to introduce simple formulae
- Construction and use of simple formulae.

Introductory activity

T-shirts

Use a ×5 number machine to develop a formula for the total cost of buying T-shirts at £5 each:

Number of T-shirts ——[×5 ⟩——▶ Total cost

giving the formula $n \times 5 = C$
which can be written as $C = n \times 5$

The formula can then be used to find the cost of different numbers of T-shirts.

Detailed notes

Q1 This data is also used in Q2 and Q3.

Panel above Q2 Although the answer can be found mentally, a formal method of recording should be used:
- write the formula
- substitute in the formula
- calculate the answer.

Q3 Remind pupils to provide a full step-by-step recording.

Additional activity

Designer T-shirts

Construct a formula for the total cost (C) in £ to produce n designer T-shirts where there is an initial design cost of £10 and a unit cost of £5 per T-shirt.

1 T-shirt costs $1 \times 5 + 10$ pounds,
2 T-shirts cost $2 \times 5 + 10$ pounds,
3 T-shirts cost $3 \times 5 + 10$ pounds, and so on, leading to the formula $C = n \times 5 + 10$.

Equipment

None.

Content

- Use of shortened algebraic form for multiplication
- Construction and use of simple formulae in symbolic form.

Detailed notes

Panel above Q1 The interpretation of '$4 \times a$' as '4 lots of a' or '$a + a + a + a$' could be included in the discussion of this notation.

Q2 Pupils who give answers in repeated addition form should also be required to give the multiplication form.

Panel above Q4 The importance of the method of recording used in the lower half of the panel should be emphasised.

Additional activity

Regular polygons

Ask pupils to construct formulae for the perimeters of different regular polygons, for example $p = 51$, $p = 61$ and so on.

Then ask them to examine their results and make a general statement about the perimeter of any regular polygon.

Equipment

None.

Content

■ Construction and use of simple formulae.

Equipment

None.

Detailed notes

Q1 Encourage pupils to use the formula in the form $p = 20a$.

Q2 Remind pupils to provide a full step-by-step recording.

E14
Formulae:
Using a
formula

UA2c/5
A3ab/5

PSE
I/E1
FE/E4

Content

■ Use of a formula and codes to find on which day of the week certain historical events took place

■ Interpretation of information in written and tabular form.

Introductory activity

Date demonstration
Give the pupils an old calendar. Ask them to choose any date and then, using the formula in the panel on E14, tell them the day of the week. Discuss the method shown on the page in detail. Further examples, perhaps drawn from sport, could be discussed. For example, Sebastian Coe's world records: the 800 m (10/6/81) and the 1000 m (11/7/81); Yvonne Murray's European Championship victory in the 3000 m (29/8/90).

Detailed notes

Q2 Other familiar events of the 1980s and 1990s could be added to this list.

Q3 Some explanation of how to identify a leap year may be necessary.
In a leap year, subtract 1 from the month codes for January and February.

Q4a The year codes table has to be extended. Pupils must identify the pattern which involves a cycle of the numbers 0 to 6, missing a number every leap year.

Q4b Pupils can either try each month in turn or use the formula to work backwards by putting $D = 13$ and $Y = 0$ so that $13 + M \div 7$ must give remainder equal to 6. Hence $M = 0$, giving April and July.

Additional activity

The 21st century
Challenge the pupils to find the day of the week of the first day of the 21st century. This may lead to some interesting discussion.

Equipment

None.

E15
Formulae: Finding a formula

A3ab/5

PSE
FE/E4

Content

- Investigation of the relationship connecting points, regions and lines in a network
- Construction and use of formulae
- Construction of networks of given specifications
- Interpretation and presentation of information in written and visual form.

Detailed notes

Panel above Q1 It may be helpful to discuss a few more examples to ensure that the definitions of point, line and region are fully understood.

Q1b The pupils should notice that the numbers in the last column are one less than the corresponding numbers in the second last column.

Q2a It is advisable to check that pupils have the correct formula before they attempt this question.

Q2b Ask pupils to compare their networks and comment on their findings.

Equipment

None.

E16
Formulae: Construction

A3ab/5

FE/E4
PFS/D1

Content

- Construction and use of formulae for perimeters of rectangles and pentagons.

Detailed notes

Q2 Encourage pupils to find and describe an alternative method of calculating the perimeter of a rectangle:

'Add the length and breadth, then multiply by 2'.

Equipment

None.

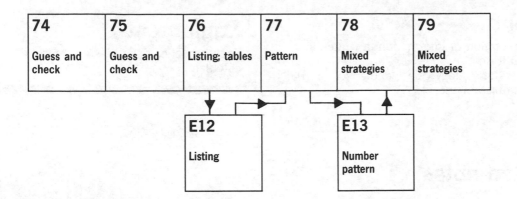

CONTENT AND DEVELOPMENT

Core

Heinemann Mathematics 7 deals with the strategies of Guess and check, Listing and Looking for a pattern.

Heinemann Mathematics 8, *Problem Solving 1* covers:

■ consolidation and development of the above strategies
■ the application of a range of strategies

and provides some mixed strategy problems.

Problem Solving 2 in *Part 3* consolidates the above strategies, introduces 'Make a model' and provides a range of mixed strategy problems.

Extension

E12 extends the listing work of Core Textbook page 76.

E13 extends the pattern work of Core Textbook page 77.

National Curriculum (England and Wales)

UA2abc, 3b, 4ab
A2b

Mathematics 5–14 (Scotland)

PSE   O/D1   AS/D2   MD/D3, 4   PS/E2
FE/D1   FE/E4   ME/D4   PFS/E1

Organisation

The work is presented as titled problems, for example Matches, Crosses, from which a selection can be made to suit differing abilities. The selection should include work from all aspects of problem solving. It is not anticipated that pupils will complete every problem in the section. It is recommended that the class is organised in groups and it is likely that a number of problems will be in use at the same time.

RELATED ACTIVITIES

Puzzle corner
The puzzle corner of magazines and newspapers often contains worthwhile problem-solving activities. Pupils could contribute to a collection of suitable problems which could be mounted on cards and used at appropriate times throughout the year.

EQUIPMENT

Spent matches, die, calculator, 1 cm square dot and 1 cm squared paper, ruler, 360° protractor, scissors, coloured pencils.

74
Problem solving 1: Guess and check

UA4b/5

**PSE
AS/D2
MD/D3**

Content

- Interpretation of information in written and visual form
- Use of the strategy Guess and check or Trial and improvement.

Equipment

Spent matches or other suitable sticks, calculator.

Detailed notes

Matches pattern The finished pattern should have no 'open' squares.

Crosses, Q1b There are many possible answers.

Crosses, Q1e 'Consecutive numbers' may need explanation.

Crosses, Q2 Each number can be used once only.

Crosses, Q3c Some pupils may realise that the total of 123 must be 3 times the sum of two consecutive numbers.

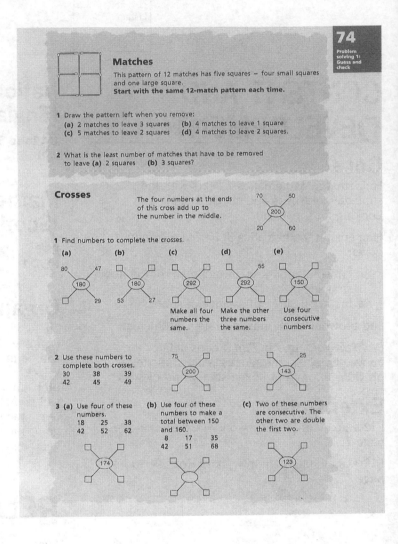

Content

- Interpretation of information in written and visual form
- Use of the strategy Guess and check.

Organisation

Pupils need to work in pairs for all *Seeing spots* work.

Introductory activities

The following activities should be used only if pupils have difficulty with the problems.

1 House numbers
Ask pupils to give examples of different house numbering systems. Discuss the picture at the top of Core Textbook page 75 to highlight how these houses are numbered.

2 An age-old problem
Use as an example a pupil with two siblings from the class and demonstrate how the problem could be calculated using their ages.

3 Seeing spots
Demonstrate how a die can be placed on a table so that the spots on only three faces can be seen.

Detailed notes

House numbers, Q1	Pupils should realise that only pairs of consecutive odd numbers need be tried.
House numbers, Q2	'Directly opposite' should be interpreted as: house number 2 is opposite house number 1 house number 4 is opposite house number 3 as illustrated.
An age-old problem, table	Several guesses may be needed. In each guess the ages must total 39 years.
Seeing Spots	It is important that the die is positioned as illustrated.

Equipment

Die, calculator.

Content

- Interpretation of information presented in tabular and written form
- Use of the strategy Listing systematically.

Detailed notes

Hare and tortoise, table	An explanation of how to find the distances may be needed.
Dice scores, table	The two colours emphasise, for example, that 1,2 and 2,1 are different outcomes.
Bags of potatoes, 3 kg table	This table could become very lengthy. Pupils could restrict entries to 1, 2, ... 10, 20, ... 50. Encourage pupils to find all three possible answers.
Team selection	A systematic form of recording is expected but not necessarily a table.

Additional activity

Tree diagram
A tree diagram layout could be constructed as a useful alternative way of recording the team selection information. The tree diagram provides a pictorial representation of a systematic listing process. For example:

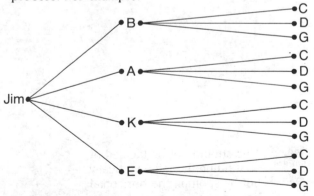

12 teams with Jim in each, and another 12 teams with Tom in each.

Equipment

None.

77
Problem
solving 1:
Pattern

UA2c/5

**PSE
O/D1
PS/E2
FE/E4
ME/D4**

Content

- Interpretation of information in tabular and visual form
- Identification, description and use of number patterns
- Area of rectangles, triangles and composite shapes by counting squares.

Introductory activity

Number patterns

Ask pupils to give examples of and describe number patterns, for example

2 4 6 8 10 12 . . . and
1 3 5 7   9 11 . . .
(house numbers in a street)

5 10 15 20 25 30 . . .
(rhymes in games).

Additional activities

1 Sums of odd numbers

Ask pupils to use the values of
$1 + 3 + 5 + \ldots + 17 + 19$ and
$1 + 3 + 5 + \ldots + 27 + 29$ to find the sum of
$21 + 23 + 25 + 27 + 29$, then challenge them to find the sum of $41 + 43 + 45 + 47 + 49$ in a similar way. Results could be checked by direct addition.

2 Sums of even numbers

The relationship between sums of even numbers and the square numbers can be investigated:

$$2 = 1^2 + 1$$
$$2 + 4 = 6 = 2^2 + 2$$
$$2 + 4 + 6 = 12 = 3^2 + 3$$
$$2 + 4 + 6 + 8 = 20 = 4^2 + 4$$

and so on.

Equipment

1 cm square dot paper.

Detailed notes

Dotty picture, Q3 Encourage pupils to use the pattern in each column as well as the row total.

Odd pattern, Q3c This should not be tackled by continuing the table vertically but by spotting the horizontal link.

Q4 Ask pupils to evaluate these sums.

Q4d Encourage pupils to find how many odd numbers are being summed without counting them, for example 'add 1 to the last number then halve'.

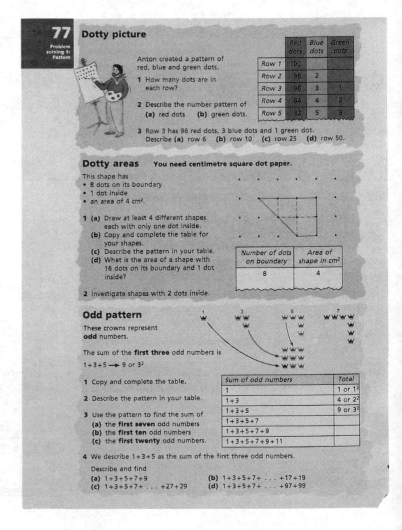

Content

- Interpretation and construction of diagrams
- Measurement to the nearest centimetre to find the area of rectangles
- Use of strategies such as Methodical working, Reasoning, Guess and check.

Detailed notes

Five squares, 2nd sentence The whole shape has to be cut into exactly five squares.

Five squares, 4th sentence Some pupils may find it helpful to start by drawing a 10 by 3 rectangle on squared paper.

Cover up, 2nd sentence The four 2 by 1 rectangles should be cut from cm squared paper. Alternatively, four dominoes, blank side up, could be used with the number square drawn to suit.

Tiling rectangles, Q1, Q2 The sides should be measured to the nearest 1 cm.

Equipment

Ruler, 1 cm squared paper, scissors, coloured pencils.

Content

- Interpretation of information in visual form
- Description and use of number patterns
- Use of the strategies Looking for a pattern and Listing systematically
- Finding all the possibilities.

Detailed notes

Sum of digits The terms 'digit' and 'sum' may require explanation.

Windows Dominoes, blank side up, could be used to demonstrate the rectangular types of windows allowed.

Windows, Q2b With only three numbers in the table, different numbers can be predicted. Many pupils will choose the doubling pattern 2, 4, 8, 16 which, they should find on checking, does not apply.

Equipment

1 cm square dot paper or dominoes.

Content

- Interpretation of information in written and tabular form
- Use of the strategy Listing systematically.

Detailed notes

Q2 A similar table to the one in Q1 is expected.

Additional activity

Holiday Excursions
Ask three pupils to choose three excursions. They should try to arrange their excursions to leave at least one day when all three pupils could go to the beach together.

Equipment

None.

E13
Problem
solving 1:
Number
pattern

UA2c, 3b/
5 → 6
A2b/5

PSE
FE/E4

Content

- Identification, description and use of a
  number pattern
- Use of the strategy Looking for a pattern.

Additional activity

Mystic roses
Ask pupils to construct other mystic roses using a
360° protractor, for example 8 equally spaced
points on the circumference, 15 points and so on.
A wall display could be made of pupils' work.

Equipment

Ruler, 360° protractor.

Detailed notes

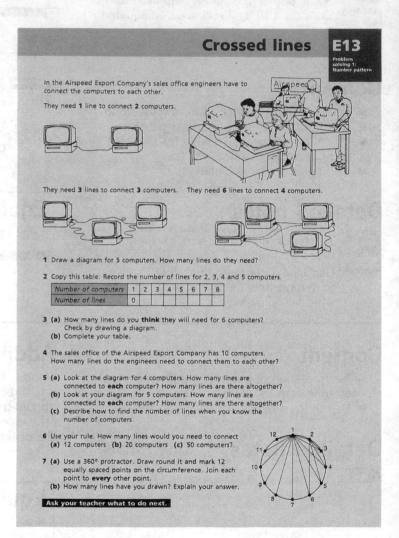

Crossed lines **E13**
Problem
solving 1:
Number pattern

In the Airspeed Export Company's sales office engineers have to
connect the computers to each other.

They need **1** line to connect **2** computers.

They need **3** lines to connect **3** computers. They need **6** lines to connect **4** computers.

1 Draw a diagram for 5 computers. How many lines do they need?

2 Copy this table. Record the number of lines for 2, 3, 4 and 5 computers.

Number of computers	1	2	3	4	5	6	7	8
Number of lines	0							

3 (a) How many lines do you **think** they will need for 6 computers?
   Check by drawing a diagram.
   (b) Complete your table.

4 The sales office of the Airspeed Export Company has 10 computers.
   How many lines do the engineers need to connect them to each other?

5 (a) Look at the diagram for 4 computers. How many lines are
   connected to **each** computer? How many lines are there altogether?
   (b) Look at your diagram for 5 computers. How many lines are
   connected to **each** computer? How many lines are there altogether?
   (c) Describe how to find the number of lines when you know the
   number of computers.

6 Use your rule. How many lines would you need to connect
   (a) 12 computers (b) 20 computers (c) 50 computers?

7 (a) Use a 360° protractor. Draw round it and mark 12
   equally spaced points on the circumference. Join each
   point to **every** other point.
   (b) How many lines have you drawn? Explain your answer.

Ask your teacher what to do next.

Q3a The assumption that a
number pattern continues
must be checked or proved.

Q5c An acceptable word formula
might be 'The number of
lines is found by multiplying
the number of computers by
the number of computers less
1 and then dividing by 2'.
Some pupils may be
challenged to give a symbolic
formula. Encourage pupils to
try and explain why the rule
works.

Q7 Pupils may be interested to
know that this pattern is
called a 'mystic rose'. There
should be discussion to
ensure the relationship with
the 'computer lines' problem
is established.

DETOURS IN PART 2

General advice about using the Detours can be found on page T6 of these Notes.

General advice about using the Detours can be found on page T6 of these Notes.

54
Detour:
Reflection and
tiling

SM3b/4

PSE
S/D2
S/E2

Content

■ Construction and extension of patterns using reflection and translation
■ Presentation of findings in visual form.

Introductory activity

Islamic-type patterns
It may be helpful to use an example like the one below to illustrate the process described on the Textbook page. Emphasise that the lines AB and PQ are axes of reflection only and that neither they nor the boundary lines form part of the final pattern.

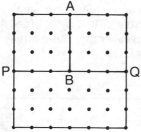
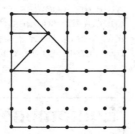

Draw three lines in top left-hand square.

Redraw the pattern without the axes of reflection or the boundary lines.
Repeat as necessary to create a tiling effect.

Detailed notes

Q2d This example involves four starting lines, one of which is curved.

Additional activity

Other axes
It is possible to produce different patterns, for example
■ by making the first axis diagonal
■ by using one reflection and one rotation.

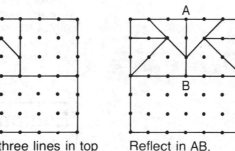
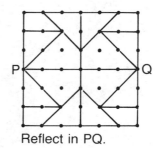

Reflect in AB.   Reflect in PQ.

Equipment

Ruler, $\frac{1}{2}$ cm square dot or squared paper, coloured pencils.

63
W19
Detour:
Investigating
diagonals

A2b/4
SM2b/4

PSE
RS/D1, 7
FE/D1

Content

■ Definition and recognition of a diagonal
■ Recognition and extension of number patterns
■ Investigation of the relationship between the number of sides of a 2D shape and
  – the number of triangles formed when the diagonals from one vertex are drawn
  – the number of diagonals needed to make the shape 'rigid'.

Introductory activity

Diagonals
Different shapes and their diagonals could be drawn and discussed. It is important the pupils realise that
■ for shapes with more than four sides, more than one diagonal can be drawn from the same vertex
■ diagonals can be drawn from different vertices.

Detailed notes

Q2d If the pupils were to add diagonals as shown opposite these would also form triangles and make the hexagon rigid.

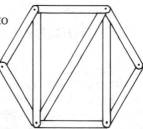

Additional activity

Rigid structures
A class collection of models or pictures from newspapers, magazines or books which show the rigidity of triangular structures would help to add interest to this work and would make an attractive display.

Equipment

Meccano or plastic or card strips, fasteners.

75

S24
Detour:
Whole
numbers

N3a/3 → 4

AS/D1
MD/C1

Content

- Mental completion of number statements involving the four operations
- Recognition and description of a number pattern.

Detailed notes

Correct the pupils' answers in the answer boxes on the page *before* allowing them to join the points using straight lines. The answers are the odd numbers from 1 to 41.

Equipment

None.

Content

- Use of coordinates in the form B3.

The pupils have to position parts of a picture correctly in order to construct the complete picture.

Additional activity

Star pictures

Grids, similar to the one shown, could be drawn over photographs of pop stars, sports people, other personalities and so on. The three-centimetre size is not crucial; a ruler width would do. Once pupils have drawn the grid they should write the 'coordinates' on each square and then cut out the squares. The squares can be shuffled and a neighbour asked to reassemble the picture by referring to the coordinates.

Equipment

Coloured pencils, scissors, glue.

S26
Detour:
, −, problem
solving

UA2abc/4
N3a/4

PSE
AS/D1

Content

- Mental addition and subtraction of whole numbers
- Use of the strategy Listing systematically.

In this number investigation pupils have to list different ways of forming a total, using a given set of numbers.

Introductory activity

Penny shoot

The shooting competition could be simulated by drawing a target on a large sheet of paper and placing it on a flat surface. Five coins, representing bullet holes, could be pushed or flicked from a marked starting point and the resulting scores totalled.

Detailed notes

Q2c All 9 cards must be considered.

Q3b Encourage pupils to list the possibilities in a systematic manner.

Additional activity

Find my score(s)

Pupils could play this game with a partner using the large paper target and pennies as in the Introductory activity. On a target, one pupil places 2, 3 or 4 coins and gives a 5-shot total. The other pupil has to find the missing scores or score.

Equipment

For the Introductory and Additional activities: large paper target, 5 pennies.

81	82	83	84
Multiples	Factors and primes	Square numbers	Cubic numbers

CONTENT AND DEVELOPMENT

Core

Heinemann Mathematics 8, *Whole numbers 1* includes place value and rounding to 10, 100, 1000, the four operations, mental multiplication and division by 10, 100, 1000, and multiples of these and estimation for multiplication and division.

Whole numbers 2 contains some consolidation of ideas introduced in earlier years and introduces some new definitions associated with numbers:

- the meanings of multiple, factor and prime number
- the meanings of square and cubic number, square and cube root
- the use of index notation for square and cubic numbers (the root symbol is *not* used).

An exploratory approach is used throughout the section and several investigations using these numbers are included. Consequently Introductory activities have not been considered appropriate and are therefore not suggested.

National Curriculum (England and Wales)

UA2bc
N3a

Mathematics 5–14 (Scotland)

MD/D1
PS/E1, 2, 3
FE/D
PM/D3
PSE
E+

RELATED ACTIVITIES

Exploring number patterns
The nature of the work lends itself to further exploration of number sets and number patterns. Most schools will have ready access to sources containing materials of this type which could be used to advantage after the work on any individual page has been completed.

Some computer software exists which allows the exploration of number patterns.

EQUIPMENT

Ruler, 1 cm squared paper, 1 cm isometric dot paper, calculator.

It may be useful to have: coins or counters to represent coins, wooden or plastic centimetre cubes.

For the Additional activity: Rubik's cube.

81
Whole
numbers 2:
Multiples

N3a/4

MD/D1
FE/D
PM/D3

Content

- Meaning and identification of sets of multiples
- Recognition and extension of a number pattern and its generalisation in words
- Use of coordinates.

Detailed notes

Top panel The facts about multiples should be discussed and linked with the set of numbers generated in Q1.

Q2 Sets of multiples can be generated using multiplication tables or by adding-on.

Q3 A check using division by 6 is expected here.

Panel above Q5 Some pupils may need help in interpreting these instructions.

Equipment

Ruler, 1 cm squared paper, 1 cm isometric dot paper.

82
Whole
numbers 2:
Factors and
primes

UA2bc/5
N3a/4

MD/D1
PS/E3
PSE

Content

- Meaning and identification of sets of factors
- Meaning and identification of prime numbers to 100
- Investigation of multiples of 2 expressed as the sum of two primes.

Detailed notes

Table beside Q1 The 2×4 rectangle in the table is regarded as the same as a 4×2 rectangle.
The facts about factors and primes in the table should be discussed.

Q5 If help is needed it could be suggested that sets of factors are listed for whole numbers 2, 3, 4, . . . , 12.

Q9 It may be necessary to remind pupils of the 'sieve' approach in Q8.

Equipment

1 cm squared paper.

83
Whole
numbers 2:
Square
numbers

N3a/4

PS/E1, 2
FE/D
PSE
E+

Content

- Meaning and identification of square numbers and square roots (the square root symbol is *not* used)
- Recognition and extension of a number pattern and its generalisation in words
- Investigation to find square numbers which when added give a third square number.

Detailed notes

Panels above Q4 and beside Q6 The facts in the panels about squares and square roots should be discussed.

Q6 It may be necessary to suggest to some pupils that they consult the table in Q5.

Q7 Pupils are likely to have difficulty explaining succinctly the *connection* between the two patterns. For any number 'multiplying 1 less than the number by 1 more than the number' gives the same answer as 'finding the square of the number then subtracting 1'.

Q8 A guess-and-check strategy is likely here. However, pupils could be encouraged to make a systematic list, for example:

$1 + 4 = 5$ $4 + 9 =$
$1 + 9 = 10$ $4 + 16 =$
$1 + 16 = 17$
. . . .

The work could be organised and shared by members of a group.

Equipment

Calculator.

Content

- Meaning and identification of cubic numbers and cube roots (the cube root symbol is *not* used)
- Recognition and extension of a number pattern and its generalisation in words
- Investigation to find sequences of odd numbers which when added give cubic numbers.

Additional activity

Rubik's cube
Some pupils may enjoy investigating this famous puzzle.

84
Whole numbers 2: Cubic numbers

UA2b/5
N3a/4

PS/E2
FE/D
PSE

Equipment

Calculator, wooden or plastic centimetre cubes may be useful.
For the Additional activity: Rubik's cube.

Detailed notes

| Panels above Q2 and beside Q4 | The facts in the panels about cubes and cube roots should be discussed. |

| Q2 | A table similar to that in Q5 on Core Textbook page 83 would be suitable. |

| Q3a | Some pupils could be asked to try $3^3 \times 4^3 \times 5^3$, which gives $(3 \times 4 \times 5)^3 \longrightarrow 60^3$. |

| Q5b | The sum could be checked using the values in the tables in Q2. |

| Q6 | The text in **bold** is intended as a hint in this investigation. |

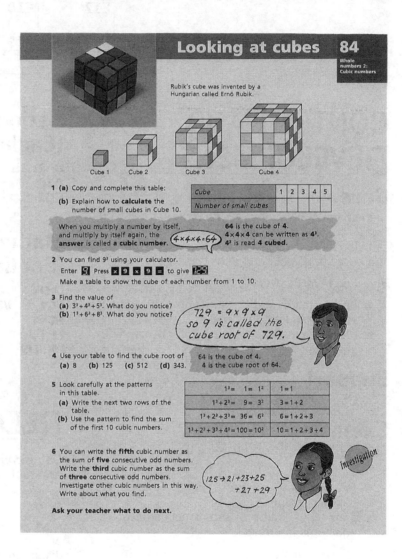

Looking at cubes 84
Whole numbers 2: Cubic numbers

Rubik's cube was invented by a Hungarian called Ernö Rubik.

Cube 1   Cube 2   Cube 3   Cube 4

1 (a) Copy and complete this table:

Cube	1	2	3	4	5
Number of small cubes					

(b) Explain how to **calculate** the number of small cubes in Cube 10.

When you multiply a number by itself, and multiply by itself again, the **answer** is called a **cubic number**. $4 \times 4 \times 4 = 64$

64 is the cube of **4**.
$4 \times 4 \times 4$ can be written as 4^3.
4^3 is read **4 cubed**.

2 You can find 9^3 using your calculator.
Enter 9 Press × 9 × 9 = to give 729
Make a table to show the cube of each number from 1 to 10.

3 Find the value of
(a) $3^3 + 4^3 + 5^3$. What do you notice?
(b) $1^3 + 6^3 + 8^3$. What do you notice?

$729 = 9 \times 9 \times 9$
so 9 is called the cube root of 729.

4 Use your table to find the cube root of
(a) 8   (b) 125   (c) 512   (d) 343.

64 is the cube of **4**.
4 is the cube root of 64.

5 Look carefully at the patterns in this table.
(a) Write the next two rows of the table.
(b) Use the pattern to find the sum of the first 10 cubic numbers.

$1^3 = 1 = 1^2$	$1 = 1$
$1^3 + 2^3 = 9 = 3^2$	$3 = 1 + 2$
$1^3 + 2^3 + 3^3 = 36 = 6^2$	$6 = 1 + 2 + 3$
$1^3 + 2^3 + 3^3 + 4^3 = 100 = 10^2$	$10 = 1 + 2 + 3 + 4$

6 You can write the **fifth** cubic number as the sum of **five** consecutive odd numbers.
Write the **third** cubic number as the sum of **three** consecutive odd numbers.
Investigate other cubic numbers in this way.
Write about what you find.

$125 \rightarrow 21 + 23 + 25 + 27 + 29$

Investigation

Ask your teacher what to do next.

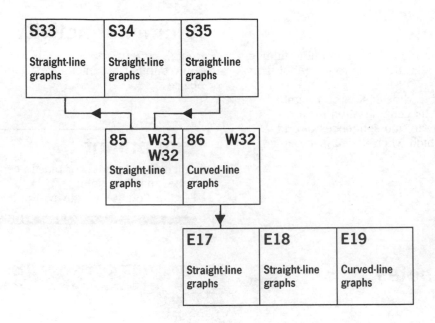

CONTENT AND DEVELOPMENT

Core

Heinemann Mathematics 8, *Handling Data 1*, in *Part 2*, contains work on bar and trend graphs, calculation of range and mean, frequency tables and continuous data and survey sheets.

Handling data 2 covers

- interpretation and construction of constant gradient straight-line graphs
- interpretation and construction of curved-line graphs.

Support

S33–S35 provide lead-in work to that of the Core.

Extension

E17–E19 provide work extending beyond the Core and include

- interpretation and construction of more complex graphs
- graphical solution of simultaneous linear equations in context.

National Curriculum (England and Wales)

UA2c,3b
A2c
HD2cf

Mathematics 5–14 (Scotland)

D/D1   **D/E1**
I/C1   **I/D**   **I/E3**
M/E1
FE/D
ME/D9
E+

RELATED ACTIVITIES

Line graphs
Ask pupils if they have used graphs in other subjects, for example conversion graphs in science or home economics (°F to °C, oz to g).

A collection of line graphs used in other subjects or from newspapers could be made and displayed.

Computer packages could be used in conjunction with the work in this section to produce and print graphs.

EQUIPMENT

Ruler, 2 mm, $\frac{1}{2}$ cm, 1 cm squared paper

For the Introductory activities: daily newspaper.

Content

- Interpretation and construction of straight-line conversion and cost graphs
- Approximate relationship between litres and gallons.

Introductory activity

Rates of exchange
A class discussion on current rates of foreign currency exchange, using figures taken from the daily newspapers, would be useful to set the scene. Details for Spain and Portugal in particular should be discussed.

Detailed notes

Q1 Some pupils may need help to calculate the value of 'one small interval' on each axis.

W31, Q3b It is important that the graph is used to find the answer and that the result is not calculated.

Additional activity

Holiday cash graph
Pupils could construct the appropriate currency conversion graph for a country of their choice, for example, one they may be visiting on holiday.

Equipment

Ruler.
For the Introductory activity: daily newspaper.
For the Additional activity: $\frac{1}{2}$ cm squared paper.

85
W31
W32
(Q1–5
Handling data 2: Straight-line graphs

A2c/5
HD2cf/
5 → 6

D/D1
D/E1
I/D
M/E1
ME/D9

Content

- Interpretation and construction of curved-line graphs.

Introductory activity

Daily temperature
The information in the table below could be used to illustrate how to draw curved-line graphs. Interpretation of the graph and a discussion of the trends could then follow.

Time	6am	7am	8am	10am	noon	1pm	3pm	5pm	7pm	9pm
Temperature °C	9	10	12	20	24	23	21	15	12	11

Detailed notes

Q1 The scale on the time axis may cause difficulty, with each small interval representing 12 minutes.

Q4 Encourage pupils to write as full a description as possible.

Q6 Some pupils may have to be alerted to the fact that there are two answers to each of these.

Q11 The pupils will need to extend the curve beyond the given values.

Equipment

2 mm squared paper.

86
W32
(Q6–8,
Handling data 2: Curved-line graphs

A2c/5
HD2cf/
5 → 6

D/D1
D/E1
I/E3

Content

- Interpretation and construction of straight-line graphs.

Introductory activity

Pupil jumps
The work could be introduced by considering a pupil who covers 2 metres with every jump.

Number of jumps	1	2	3	4	5
Distance in metres	2	4	6	8	10

Use these results to draw a graph and discuss
- the fact that a graph should have a title
- the labelling of both axes
- the way the scales are numbered on the lines and not in between
- the interpretation of the graph from either axis
- the origin is a point on the graph 'in 0 jumps the distance is 0 metres'.

Detailed notes

Q3 Pupils may need help with the numbering and labelling of the axes.

Equipment

Ruler, $\frac{1}{2}$ cm or 1 cm squared paper.

S33
Handling data 2: Straight-line graphs

A2c/5
HD2cf/4

D/D1
I/C1

S34
Handling
data 2:
Straight-line
graphs

A2c/5
HD2cf/4

D/D1
I/C1

Content

■ Interpretation and construction of straight-line graphs.

Detailed notes

Q1a Some pupils may need help to calculate the value of 'one small interval' on each axis.

Q2b Advise pupils that if the points do not lie in a straight line, they should
■ check the calculation in their table
■ check that all points have been plotted correctly.
Some pupils may need to be reminded to extend the graph to the origin.

Equipment

Ruler.

S35
Handling
data 2:
Straight line
graphs

A2c/5
HD2cf/4

D/D1
I/C1

Content

■ Interpretation and construction of straight-line graphs.

Introductory activity

Stamps graph
The work could be introduced by considering a pupil who buys a number of 10 pence stamps.

Number of stamps	1	2	3	4	5
Cost in pence	10	20	30	40	50

Use these results to draw a graph and discuss
■ the fact that a graph should have a title
■ the labelling of both axes
■ the way the scales are numbered on the lines and not in between
■ the interpretation of the graph from either axis
■ the origin is a point on the graph.

Additional activity

Crisps
Ask pupils to look at costs which would involve more difficult arithmetic, for example, costs of bags of crisps at, say, 22 pence.

Equipment

Ruler, $\frac{1}{2}$ cm squared paper.
For the Introductory activity: 2mm squared paper.

E17
Handling
data 2:
Straight-line
graphs

UA2c, 3b/5
A2c/5
HD2cf/
5 → 6

D/D1
D/E1
FE/D
ME/D9

Content

■ Construction and interpretation of straight-line graphs.
The graphs do not pass through the origin.

Detailed notes

Q1 Pupils should be aware that 1 pound is just under half a kilogram. They may need to be reminded of the abbreviation (lb) for pounds.

Q5c Pupils will need to extend the graph produced in Q4 to find the answer.

Q6 Some pupils may not realise that information needs to be taken from the graphs produced in Q1 and Q4.

Q7 Different strategies can be used here, for example:
■ investigating number patterns
■ extending the graph to meet the time axis.

It is worthwhile discussing the realistic minimum weight for cooking a chicken and therefore to what extent extrapolation is meaningful.

Equipment

Ruler, 2 mm squared paper.

Content

- Interpretation and construction of straight-line graphs
- Graphical solution of two simultaneous linear equations.

Introductory activity

Which photocopier?
It may be necessary to set the scene by considering, for example, photocopying charges for two different machines.

A: 10p + 1p per copy   B: 2p per copy.

Copies	2	4	6	8	10	12	14
A	12p	14p	16p	18p	20p	22p	24p
B	4p	8p	12p	16p	20p	24p	28p
Cheaper	B	B	B	B	Same	A	A

Discuss the cheaper machine for each number of copies.

Demonstrate how to graph the information and discuss how the same results can be obtained from the graph.

Detailed notes

Q5 Refer to the point where the lines cross and its significance.

Ask pupils to give as full an explanation as they can. It is likely that pupils will choose the cheaper plumber; however, it is worth discussing other considerations, for example, quality of work, reliability, how quickly the job can be started, how long the job will take.

Additional activity

Which car?
Ask pupils to consider three different systems of charges for hiring a car for a week and to investigate the cheapest system for different mileages:
A – £10 fixed charge plus 10p per mile
B – £15 fixed charge plus 5p per mile
C – £25 fixed charge, no mileage charge.

A table and graph should be drawn to illustrate the situation, using intervals of 20 miles.

Equipment

Ruler, 2 mm squared paper.

E18
Handling data 2: Straight-line graphs

A2c/6 → 7
HD2cf/ 5 → 6

D/D1
I/D
I/E3
E+

Content

- Interpretation and construction of curved-line graphs.

Detailed notes

First sentence above graph Ensure that pupils are familiar with immersion heating, for example the element in an electric kettle, and discuss why the water temperature did not start at 0°C.

Q4 Ensure the pupils realise that:
- 1 small interval on the time axis represents 6 seconds
- 1 small interval on the temperature axis represents 1°C.

Ask pupils to draw as smooth a curve as they can.

Additional activity

Cooling curve
The following workcard could be used to provide another opportunity for pupils to draw a curved-line graph of a different type.

The beaker of hot water was allowed to cool. The table shows the recorded temperatures:

Time (minutes)	0	5	10	15	20	25	30	35	40	45	50
Temperature (°C)	100	75	57	44	34	27	22	19	17	16	16

(a) Draw a graph using these scales:
Time axis – 2 cm represents 5 minutes
Temperature axis – 1 cm represents 10°C
(b) How long did it take for the water to cool to ■ 50°C ■ 25°C?
(c) Why did the temperature not fall below 16°C?

Equipment

2 mm squared paper.

E19
Handling data 2: Curved-line graphs

A2c/5
HD2cf/ 5 → 6

D/D1
D/E1

FRACTIONS 2

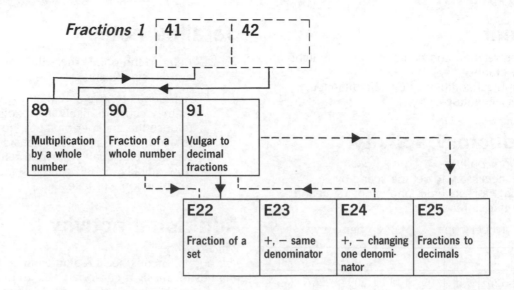

CONTENT AND DEVELOPMENT

Core

Heinemann Mathematics 8, *Fractions 1*, deals with informal multiplication and division with fractions, one quantity as a fraction of another and equivalence.

Fractions 2 consolidates and develops:

- multiplication of a fraction by a whole number
- multiplication of a mixed number by a whole number
- a fraction of a quantity
- conversion of a fraction to a decimal.

Support

Pupils who have done only Support material in *Fractions 1* should be directed to *Fractions 1*, Core Textbook pages 41 and 42, before attempting this section.

Extension

The additional work on pages E22–E25 includes:

- +, − with same denominator
- +, − with one denominator a multiple of the other
- interpretation and construction of a curved-line conversion graph for fractions to decimals.

This work can be attempted after the Core Textbook pages or alternatively this section can be used in two separate parts:

Core Textbook pages 89, 90 linked to E22 – E24 and Core Textbook page 91 linked to E25.

National Curriculum (England and Wales)

N2b, 3cd, 4a

Mathematics 5–14 (Scotland)

D/E1
RTN/D3   RTN/E2
FPR/D   FPR/E1, 3, 4, 5
ME/D5
E+

RELATED ACTIVITIES

The world of fractions
Encourage pupils to collect examples of the use of fractions in the world around them, for example, newspapers, advertisements, work in other subjects and so on. The examples tend to be limited and confined to simple fractions.

EQUIPMENT

Calculator, 2 mm squared paper.

For the Introductory activity: advertising posters.

84

89
Fractions 2:
Multiplication
by a whole
number

N2b, 3c,
4a/5

RTN/D3
FPR/D
FPR/E3
E+

Content

- Multiplication of a fraction by a whole number
- Multiplication of a mixed number by a whole number
- Interpretation of information in written form.

Detailed notes

Panel Cuttings Ensure pupils realise that the information they need to answer Q2–Q7 is to be found in the newspaper cutting above Q1.

Q7 Some help with the interpretation of 'time and a half' and 'time and a quarter' may be needed.

Additional activity

Another method of multiplying
An alternative method of multiplying could be used, for example:

$$7 \times 2\tfrac{3}{4}$$
$$= 7 \times \tfrac{11}{4}$$
$$= \tfrac{77}{4}$$
$$= 19\tfrac{1}{4}$$

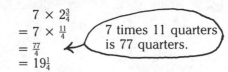
7 times 11 quarters is 77 quarters.

Equipment

None.

90
Fractions 2:
Fraction of a
whole number

N2b, 3c,
4a/5

RTN/D3
FPR/E3, 5

Content

- Fraction of a quantity
- Interpretation of information in written form.

Introductory activity

At the sales
Real-life advertising posters with $\tfrac{1}{2}$ off, $\tfrac{1}{3}$ off, $\tfrac{1}{4}$ off, and the original price could be used to set the scene. Sale price could be calculated as shown in the panel.

Detailed notes

Newspaper cuttings above Q1 The use of percentages to indicate price reductions may distract some pupils. They must realise that they should calculate using the fractions of quantities.

Q5c Able pupils could also be asked to find the *fraction* of parents who did not reply.

Equipment

For the Introductory activity: advertising posters.

91
Fractions 2:
Vulgar to
decimal
fractions

N2b/6

RTN/E2
E+

Content

- Conversion of fractions to decimals using paper and pencil and calculator techniques
- Investigation of recurring patterns in decimals.

Introductory activity

Fractions to decimals
Ask pupils to
- copy these diagrams

one biscuit

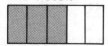

three biscuits

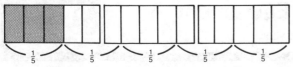

$\tfrac{1}{5}$ $\tfrac{1}{5}$ $\tfrac{1}{5}$ $\tfrac{1}{5}$ $\tfrac{1}{5}$

- shade $\tfrac{3}{5}$ of the single biscuit
- shade $\tfrac{1}{5}$ of the three biscuits
- compare the shaded parts.

The discussion should establish that

$$\tfrac{3}{5} \text{ of } 1 = \tfrac{1}{5} \text{ of } 3$$

and this can be calculated as

$$3 \div 5 \longrightarrow 5\overline{)3{\cdot}0}^{\,0{\cdot}6} = 0{\cdot}6$$

The examples at the top of the page could then be discussed and the rule for finding the decimal form introduced.

Detailed notes

Q3b Some calculators show the final digit rounded up.

Q6 Display of the eighth decimal place, not shown on most calculators, would help to show the pattern. Pupils should be able to appreciate that the display shows the start of a pattern which continues without end.

Equipment

Calculator.

E22
Fractions 2: Fraction of a set

N2b, 3cd/5

RTN/E2
FPR/E1, 4
E+

Content

- One number/quantity as a fraction of another including examples with mixed units (£ and p, m and cm)
- Expressing a fraction in its simplest form.

Detailed notes

Sentence above Q1	This information is used in Q1, 2 and 3.
Q4	The simplest form is expected. Sometimes two steps may be necessary to achieve this, for example: $\frac{45}{60} = \frac{9}{12} = \frac{3}{4}$
Panel above Q6	Pupils should realise that the units have to be the same before trying to simplify.

Equipment

None.

E23
Fractions 2: +, − same denominator

N3c/5 → 6

RTN/E2
ME/D5
E+

Content

- Interpretation of a bar graph
- Addition and subtraction of fractions and mixed numbers, with the same denominators.

Introductory activities

1 Addition
It may be necessary to revise addition of simple fractions and mixed numbers with denominators that are the same, for example:

$\frac{1}{8} + \frac{3}{8} =$ $1\frac{3}{10} + 4\frac{1}{10} =$

Examples in which the fractional parts total more than 1, should also be discussed, for example:

$\frac{4}{5} + \frac{3}{5} =$ $3\frac{7}{8} + 1\frac{5}{8} =$

2 Subtraction
Subtraction examples which require one whole to be 'exchanged' should be discussed, for example:

$$4\frac{1}{5} - 1\frac{3}{5}$$
$$= 3\frac{1}{5} - \frac{3}{5}$$
$$= 2\frac{6}{5} - \frac{3}{5}$$
$$= 2\frac{3}{5}$$

Detailed notes

Q4	Pupils may need to be reminded to give their answers in simplest form.

Equipment

None.

E24
Fractions 2: +, − changing one denominator

N3c/6

RTN/E2
E+

Content

- Addition and subtraction of fractions and mixed numbers with one denominator a multiple of the other.

Detailed notes

Panels above Q1 and Q2	This is likely to be new work for most children.
Q2	Some help may be necessary with the interpretation of the table.

Equipment

None.

Content

- Conversion of fractions to decimals using mental, written and calculator techniques
- Rounding to two decimal places
- Interpretation and construction of a curved-line conversion graph.

E25
Fractions 2:
Fractions to
decimals

N2b, 3c/6

D/E1
RTN/E2
E+

Equipment

Calculator, 2 mm squared paper.

Additional activity

A closer look at the graphs

- The fractions which were not plotted when pupils drew their graphs, for example, $\frac{2}{12}$, $\frac{2}{14}$, $\frac{2}{16}$, ... can be read off in decimal form and the values found can be compared with those for the equivalent fractions $\frac{1}{6}$, $\frac{1}{7}$, $\frac{1}{8}$, ... in the graph given in Q2.
- The shape of the graphs can be discussed further. For example, as the denominators become larger the decimal forms become smaller and the curve approaches the 'denominator axis'. Would the curve ever meet this axis?

Detailed notes

Panel above Q1 This is a reminder of the method used on Core Textbook page 91 for changing a fraction to a decimal and of the terms 'numerator' and 'denominator'.

Q1 These fractions are plotted on the graph in Q2.

Q3 After rounding, different vulgar fractions may be 'equal' when in decimal form, for example, $\frac{1}{16}$, $\frac{1}{17}$, $\frac{1}{18}$. Pupils may be able to round to three decimal places.

Q4b Unless a large sheet of 2 mm squared paper is available, a different scale will be required on the horizontal axis from that shown in Q2.

Q4c Pupils may notice that
- the graphs in Q2 and Q4 are the same shape
- for fractions with the same denominator, the decimal in the graph is double the decimal in the graph at Q2. For example, for $\frac{1}{9}$ and $\frac{2}{9}$ the decimal forms are 0·11 and 0·22 respectively.

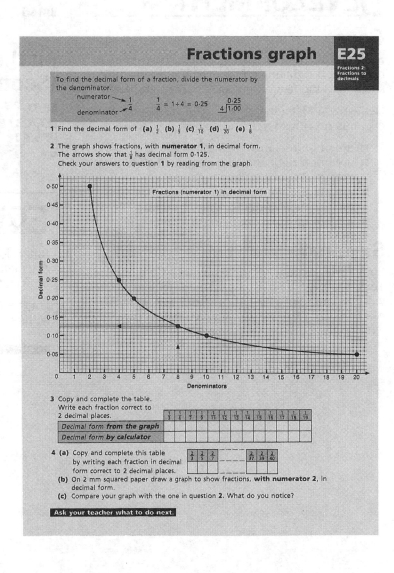

AREA

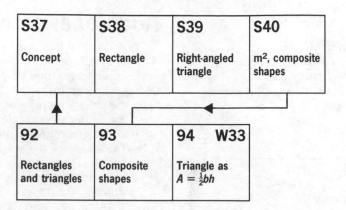

S37	S38	S39	S40
Concept	Rectangle	Right-angled triangle	m², composite shapes

92	93	94 W33
Rectangles and triangles	Composite shapes	Triangle as $A = \frac{1}{2}bh$

CONTENT AND DEVELOPMENT

Core

Heinemann Mathematics 7 includes the area of a rectangle, a right-angled triangle and an irregular shape and the use of cm², m², hectare and km².

Heinemann Mathematics 8 consolidates and expands previous work and covers:

- area of a rectangle using $A = lb$
- area of a right-angled triangle as half the area of its surrounding rectangle
- area of a composite shape made from rectangles and right-angled triangles
- area of any triangle using $A = \frac{1}{2}bh$.

Support

Pupils who experience difficulty with Core Textbook page 92 may use S37–S40 as lead-in work before returning to Core Textbook page 93. Alternatively these pages may be used as parallel work to the Core.

National Curriculum (England and Wales)

SM4d

Mathematics 5–14 (Scotland)

FE/D
ME/C3, 5, 7   ME/D1, 4, 6   ME/E2, 4
PFS/E1
E+

EQUIPMENT

Ruler, long metric tape, 4 metre sticks, calculator, tracing paper, 1 cm squared paper or acetate sheet, coloured pencils.

For the Additional activity: protractor or set square.

Content

- Area of a rectangle using $A = lb$
- Area of a right-angled triangle as half the area of its surrounding rectangle.

Detailed notes

Grid above Q1 The pupils should realise that each small square represents a tile of side 1 cm.

Q2b The 'green wall' includes the door and the windows.

Q2c The 'whole roof' consists of *two* identical tiled rectangles.

Equipment

None.

Content

- Area of a composite shape made from rectangles and right-angled triangles.

Introductory activity

Composite shape
Discuss the area of this composite shape:

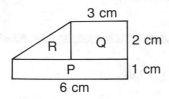

Area of rectangle P   = 6×1 =   6 cm²
Area of rectangle Q   = 3×2 =   6 cm²
Area of triangle R   = $\frac{1}{2} \times 3 \times 2$ =   3 cm²
Area of whole shape   = $\overline{15 \text{ cm}^2}$

Detailed notes

Q2 Encourage pupils to record in a systematic manner similar to the layout used for Q1.

Additional activity

Designing a panel
Pupils could design a stained glass panel of their own and find its area.

Equipment

For the Additional activity: coloured pencils.

Content

- Area of any triangle using $A = \frac{1}{2}bh$
- Investigation to find the area of an obtuse-angled triangle by a subtraction method and linking the result to the formula.

Organisation

Q1 and Q2 and the information in the panel below Q2 should be used as the basis for class discussion.

Detailed notes

W33, Q2b Pupils should realise that even if the height is 'outside' the obtuse-angled triangle the formula $A = \frac{1}{2}bh$ still applies.

Additional activity

An alternative method
For one or two examples from Q1 on W33 pupils could be asked to

- measure the longest side as base
- draw and measure the corresponding height
- calculate the area using $A = \frac{1}{2}bh$
- compare this area with that found using the subtraction method.

94
W33
Area:
Triangle as
$A = \frac{1}{2}bh$

SM4d/6

PFS/E1
E+

Equipment

For the Additional activity: calculator, ruler, protractor or set square.

S37
**Area:
Concept**

SM4d4

**ME/C3, 7
ME/D4, 6**

Content

- Area of a shape by counting squares, approximating where necessary
- Construction on centimetre squared paper of different shapes
  – with given area
  – with the same area.

Introductory activity

Labels
Ask pupils to bring in labels from bottles, tins and jars. These could be used to generate discussion of shape and relative size. A 1 cm grid on acetate sheet could be superimposed on the labels and the area of each found. Emphasise that
- 'area' means the amount of surface
- area can be measured by counting squares.

Detailed notes

Q3, last two labels Pupils should devise their own methods for dealing with the parts of the Baked Beans and French dressing labels which do not fit the grid squares. They should be asked to describe their methods.

Q5 The designs could be contextualised, coloured and displayed.

Equipment
Tracing paper, coloured pencils, 1 cm squared paper or acetate sheet.

S38
**Area:
Rectangle**

**SM4d/
5 → 6**

**FE/D
ME/C3
PFS/E1**

Content

- Area of a rectangle by counting squares
- Area of a rectangle using length × breadth.

Additional activity

Designing stamps
Pupils could design their own stamps of a given area, for example 8 cm² or 12 cm². This could be extended to finding as many different stamps as possible which have the same given area, say 24 cm².

Equipment
Ruler.

S39
**Area:
Right-angled
triangle**

**SM4d/
5 → 6**

**FE/D
ME/C3
ME/D4
PFS/E1**

Content

- Area of a right-angled triangle as half the area of its surrounding rectangle.

Detailed notes

Q3 Encourage pupils to record their calculations of the areas of sails (b) – (h) in the same systematic manner as is used for sail (a). Some pupils may wish to draw the surrounding rectangle in each example. They should be encouraged to attempt some examples without doing so.

Additional activity

Designing sails
Ask pupils to design and colour model sails of their own with a given area of, for example, 6 cm² or 15 cm².

Equipment
Ruler.
For the Additional activity: coloured pencils.

S40
**Area:
m², composite
shapes**

SM4d/6

**ME/C5
ME/D1
ME/E2, 4
PFS/E1
E+**

Content

- Estimation of lengths in metres and areas in square metres
- Area of a composite shape made from rectangles and right-angled triangles.

Detailed notes

Q1 Pupils could be asked to estimate then check how many of them can stand comfortably in a one-metre square.

Additional activity

How many pupils in the school hall?
Pupils could estimate the length and breadth of a rectangular area such as the school hall, check by measuring then calculate the floor area in m². Using their results and their knowledge of how many pupils can stand in a one-metre square they could estimate how many pupils could attend an assembly in the hall.

Equipment
A long metric tape, 4 metre sticks, calculator.

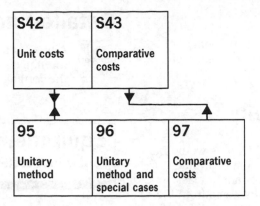

CONTENT AND DEVELOPMENT

Core

Heinemann Mathematics 7 contains work on direct proportion by the unitary method and division and multiplication by single digit numbers.

Heinemann Mathematics 8, *Proportion 1*, covers:

- direct proportion by the unitary method and 'multiple' methods
- application of direct proportion calculations to compare costs.

Proportion 2, in *Part 4*, deals with direct proportion using the calculator and the construction and interpretation of straight-line graphs representing two quantities in direct proportion.

Support

S42 and S43 provide lead-in material to Core Textbook pages 95 and 97 respectively.

National Curriculum (England and Wales)

N2b, 3c, 4a

Mathematics 5–14 (Scotland)

RTN/C3
MD/C3   MD/D1, 4   MD/E1, 2
FPR/E5
PSE

EQUIPMENT

For the Introductory activity: DIY leaflets.

95
Proportion 1:
Unitary
method

N2b, 3c,
4a/6

MD/D1
FPR/E5

Content

- Direct proportion by the unitary method
- Division and multiplication of single digit numbers.

Introductory activity

DIY leaflets
Some discussion about local DIY stores would be useful to set the scene. Stores often distribute catalogue-type advertising leaflets and a class set of these would be useful. Various items from the leaflet could be selected which refer to different units of measure as well as number and money. These could be used to create introductory examples similar to those on the textbook page.

Encourage pupils to lay out the problems as shown in the teaching panels.

Detailed notes

Panel above Q1 Although the answer could be found mentally, pupils are expected to follow the formal method of recording.

Equipment

For the Introductory activity: DIY leaflets.

96
Proportion 1:
Unitary
method and
special cases

N2b, 3c,
4a/6

MD/D1
MD/E1, 2
FPR/E5

Content

- Direct proportion by the unitary method and 'multiple' methods
- Division and multiplication by up to two-digit numbers.

Detailed notes

Panel above Q1 Revision of division by multiples of 10 may be necessary.

Q1d The cost of one, 1·4p, should not be rounded. Pupils could be asked to suggest what they might have to pay for 1 screw (for example, 2p at least, probably more). Indeed it may not be possible to purchase a screw singly.

Q4 Pupils should use the 'multiple' method.

Equipment

None.

97
Proportion 1:
Comparative
costs

N2b, 3c,
4a/6

MD/D1
FPR/E5
PSE

Content

- Application of direct proportion calculations to compare costs
- Interpretation of information in written and visual forms.

Introductory activity

Best buys
Discuss the idea of a best buy using an example like the following.

Paint is priced at:

$\frac{1}{2}$ litre tin for £1.15
1 litre tin for £2.15
3 litre tin for £6.24

- Which is the better buy? When comparing two of the above sizes, it is possible to do so by multiplying or dividing to achieve equal quantities. When comparing all three sizes, one possibility is to find the cost per litre for all three, involving a division and a multiplication.
- If the 3 litre tin is better value, why might you buy the paint in 1 litre tins?

Detailed notes

Q4b It is cheaper to buy 12 than 11. Some pupils may think they have to buy exactly 11.

Q6 Class discussion should determine various possible answers and reasons.

Equipment

None.

Content

- Direct proportion by the unitary method
- Division and multiplication of single-digit numbers.

Introductory activity

DIY leaflets
Refer to the notes for the Introductory activity on Core Textbook page 95.

Detailed notes

Q1 All the calculation is in pence to avoid using decimals.

Q2, Steaks Pupils could work this example in pounds.

Equipment

For the Introductory activity: DIY leaflets.

S42
Proportion 1:
Unit costs

N3c/5 → 6

RTN/C3
MD/C3
FPR/E5

Content

- Application of direct proportion calculations to compare costs
- Interpretation of information in written and visual forms.

Detailed notes

Panel above Q1 Reasons why people might prefer to buy items in bulk could be discussed.
Comparisons are made by multiplying up the cost of the smaller item.
It may be necessary to remind pupils of the relationships between kg/g, l/ml and m/cm.

Q7 Pupils may decide to multiply up to 3 kg and 50 packs respectively, but a variety of alternative methods may be used.

Equipment

None.

S43
Proportion 1
Comparative costs

N3c/5 → 6

RTN/C3
MD/C3
MD/D1
FPR/E5

98	W24	99		100		101	W26 W27
Nets		Pyramids and prisms		Faces, vertices, edges		Problem solving	

CONTENT AND DEVELOPMENT

Core

In Heinemann Mathematics 7 prisms and pyramids are made using nets and matching faces are stuck together to make more complicated 3D shapes.

Heinemann Mathematics 8 develops this work and includes

- recognition of 3D shapes, prisms, pyramids, and spheres, from drawings
- definition of prisms and pyramids by considering cross-sectional slices
- identification and naming of 3D shapes
- relationship among faces, vertices, edges, as Euler's formula
- pyramid and cube dissection puzzles.

National Curriculum (England and Wales)

UA2c
SM2ab

Mathematics 5–14 (Scotland)

FE/D1   FE/E4
RS/C1, 3   RS/D1, 2, 3   RS/E4
S/D2
PSE

RELATED ACTIVITIES

Collecting 3D shapes
Collections of boxes and cartons used in the environment can make an interesting display. Quite a variety of 3D shapes are used to package household items, chocolates, cosmetics and so on. Such a collection can then be classified into prisms, pyramids, spheres and others.

EQUIPMENT

Card, scissors, sticky tape, compasses, coloured pencils, a variety of 3D shapes.

Content

- Recognition of 3D shapes, prisms and pyramids, from drawings
- Construction of these shapes from nets.

Organisation

The work should be carried out in groups of about six with each pupil making perhaps two or three shapes. A complete set of the shapes should be kept for use with Core Textbook pages 99 and 100.

The templates on W24 are easier to use if the whole page is cut out. Decisions have to be made about which vertices are required for each particular shape. Making the complete net of a shape can be wasteful of card; cutting out individual faces from smaller pieces of card and sticking them together to make the net is usually more economic.

Introductory activity

Making a net
A set of commercially produced shapes could be used to revise names of shapes. The teacher could:

- discuss the shapes which are to be made
- revise what is meant by a net, for example by cutting along appropriate edges of a cube
- show how to transfer a template to card by using compasses to prick through at its vertices and joining the points in order
- discuss how to make nets using the set of 10 cm templates provided on W24
- encourage the most economical positioning of the template on the card.

Equipment

Card, scissors, sticky tape, compasses, coloured pencils.

**98
W24**
3D Shape:
Nets

SM2b/5

**RS/C1, 3
RS/D2, 3
RS/E4**

Content

- Definition of pyramids and prisms by considering cross-sectional slices
- Recognition of 3D shapes, prisms, pyramids and spheres, from drawings
- Identification and naming of 3D shapes.

Introductory activities

1 Identification of pyramids and prisms

- Ask the pupils to imagine that a hexagonal prism is cut into slices in a butcher's or grocer's slicing machine. What can you say about the slices? They are all the same size and shape; they are identical (the term 'congruent' could be used).
- What would happen if a triangular pyramid were sliced in the machine? Pupils should be able to say that the slices are all the same shape but their sizes are decreasing (or increasing).
- Is every shape a prism or a pyramid? What would happen to a sphere in the slicing machine?

2 Language and terminology
Ask the pupils to describe the slices that would arise when certain other familiar solids were sliced in the machine. This should lead to the use of alternative names for some of these solids, for example:

cuboid ──→ square or rectangular prism
cylinder ──→ circular prism
cone ──→ circular pyramid.

Detailed notes

Q1 The shapes should at least include those from Core Textbook page 98.

Q4 The lamp shades with pieces missing from the top may confuse some pupils. It is not intended to teach about truncated solids at this stage. Their recording should say 'square pyramid, not complete' or 'top missing'.

Equipment

A variety of solid shapes including those constructed for Core Textbook page 98.

99
3D Shape:
Pyramids and
prisms

**SM2a/6;
2b/5**

**RS/C1, 3
RS/D2**

100
3D Shape:
Faces,
vertices,
edges

SM2a/6

RS/C3
RS/D1
FE/D1
FE/E4

Content

- Identification of faces, vertices and edges
- Relationship among faces, vertices, edges, as Euler's formula
- Recognition of 3D shapes, prisms and pyramids, from drawings.

Introductory activity

Faces, vertices and edges
The panel at the top of the page provides a reminder of the names used for parts of solid shapes and most pupils would benefit from a discussion of these names. In particular, some pupils have difficulty using vertex for corner and can also be confused by vertex and vertices.

The ideas concerning prisms and pyramids which were introduced on Core Textbook page 99 could be revised. A table like the one in Q1 could be drawn and some pupils invited to fill in the first line or two.

Detailed notes

Q1b The formula might be written as $f + v = e + 2$ or $f + v - e = 2$ or be given in word form.

Q1c Leonhard Euler (1707–1783), pronounced 'Oiler' was one of the most prolific mathematicians in history. He discovered the relationship $f + v = e + 2$ in 1752. Although it was actually known earlier than this his name has been given to the 'formula'.

Q2 Models of shapes I to O should be on display.

Q4b A full description is intended, for example, 'shapes with more than 6 faces **and** with 1 or more triangular faces'.

Additional activity

Exploring Euler's formula
Other shapes collected for Core Textbook page 99 could be investigated to see if they comply with Euler's formula.

Equipment

A variety of solid shapes including those constructed for Core Textbook page 98 and a cube.

101
W26
W27
3D Shape:
Problem
solving

UA2c/5
SM2b/6

RS/C3
RS/E4
PSE

Content

- Construction of 3D shapes from nets and by joining 3D shapes at matching faces
- Recognition of 3D shapes, pyramids, from drawings.

Organisation

The work could be attempted by groups of 2, 3, 5 and 6 for the red, blue, green and yellow puzzles respectively to spread the workload. The red puzzle is the simplest. On completion each group's puzzle could be used by the other groups. All these puzzles are well known and may be available as plastic shapes.

Equipment

Card, scissors, compasses, sticky tape.

VOLUME

CONTENT AND DEVELOPMENT

Heinemann Mathematics 7 includes work on the relationship between the millilitre and cubic centimetre, reading scales in millilitres and finding volumes by counting cubes and using the formula $V = l \times b \times h$.

Heinemann Mathematics 8 includes:

- volumes of cuboids and cubes using displacement and $V = l \times b \times h$
- use of nets to construct different open cuboids of equal volume
- relationship among units – cm³, m³, ml, l
- identification and drawing of cross-sections of prisms
- area of the cross-section by counting squares
- volume of a prism by counting cubes and as the area of cross-section × height.

National Curriculum (England and Wales)

UA2b
A3b
SM4abd

Mathematics 5–14 (Scotland)

FE/D1
ME/C3, 6   ME/D1, 3   ME/E4, 5, 6, 7
PFS/E2
RS/D6   RS/C1, 3
PSE
E+

RELATED ACTIVITIES

Volume units in the environment
Pupils could collect items for class display, which are marked or labelled with words, units and abbreviations associated with volume. Some of these units may not appear in this section. Pupils could give examples of volume used in other subject areas such as science, home economics or technology.

EQUIPMENT

Toothpaste box marked in millilitres, card, ruler, scissors, sticky tape, metre sticks, drawing pins, string, long metric tapes, trundle wheel, squared paper ($\frac{1}{2}$ or 1 cm).

For the Introductory/Additional activities: cup, 1-litre container, measuring jar or jug, cuboids made from plasticine/fired clay, water or sand, 1 cm cubes, perspex/cardboard box, a variety of solids (including prisms), medicine bottle, juice cartons (cuboids).

103
Volume:
Reading
scales, ml,
cm³

SM4ab/4

ME/C6
ME/D3
ME/E6
PSE

Content

- Reading scales marked in 100 millimetre intervals with subdivisions of 10 ml, 25 ml
- Relationship between millilitres/litres and millilitres/cubic centimetres
- Calculation of volume using displacement.

Introductory activities

Sand can provide a useful dry replacement for water in some activities, and should be settled by tapping the container on a flat surface.

1 How much is a cupful?
Pupils could find the number of cupfuls that can be filled by a 1-litre container and use this to estimate the volume of the cup. Estimates can be checked using a measuring jar.

2 Displacement
Pupils could find the volumes of cuboids made from plasticine/fired clay using $V = l \times b \times h$. These volumes can be compared with displacement using a measuring jar partially filled with water.

Detailed notes

`Q4a` Pupils may need to be reminded that the scale should be read at the lowest level of the meniscus.

Additional activity

Ugh – how long will it last?
Pupils could use a measuring jar to find the volume of a medicine bottle filled with water. A medicine spoon has a volume of 5 ml. Ask pupils to find how long the medicine will last for different prescribed doses, for example '2 spoonsful 3 times a day'.

Equipment

For the Introductory activities: cup, litre container, measuring jar or jug, cuboids made from plasticine/fired clay, water or sand.
For the Additional activity: medicine bottle, measuring jar or jug, water or sand.

104
Volume:
Cuboid,
$V = l \times b \times h$

SM4d/6

ME/D3
PFS/E2
RS/D6
PSE

Content

- Volumes of a cuboid and a cube using $V = l \times b \times h$
- Relationship between 1 millilitre and 1 cubic centimetre
- Use of nets to construct different open cuboids of equal volume.

Organisation

Group work is required for Q4 and Q5 and for Introductory activity 1.

Introductory activities

1 Making cuboids
Issue pupils with 24 × 1 cm cubes and ask them to make as many different cuboids as possible using all 24 cubes. The length, breadth and height of each cuboid could be recorded in a table.

2 How much in the box?
Give pupils a Perspex/cardboard box that can be packed tightly with 1 cm cubes and ask them to find the volume of the box using the cubes. The volume could then be found in millilitres by filling the box with water/sand and pouring the contents into a measuring jar.

Detailed notes

`Q4c` The pupils could discuss the discrepancy. In fact the volume marked on the box refers to the volume of the toothpaste in the tube and not to the volume of the box itself.

`Q5b, c` In practice the pupils have to find three whole numbers whose product is 64.

Additional activity

Why the difference?
Ask pupils to measure empty juice cartons (cuboids) and work out their volumes. They ought to find that their answer is greater than the marked volume. A discussion could follow about why the volume of the container is greater than the volume of the contents.

Equipment

Toothpaste box marked in millilitres, card, ruler, scissors, sticky tape.
For the Introductory activities: 1 cm cubes, perspex/cardboard box, measuring jar or jug, water or sand.
For the Additional activity: juice cartons (cuboids).

Content

- Volume of a cuboid in cubic metres, m^3, using $V = l \times b \times h$
- Relationship between weight and volume of water
- Relationship among units – cm^3, m^3, l

Organisation

For Q1 and Q2 pupils are required to work in groups.

Detailed notes

Q1b Pupils could first be asked to *estimate* how many pupils would fit inside the metre cube.

Panel above Q1b This is intended to convey the idea that 1 cubic metre can have an infinite variety of shapes.

Q2b Encourage pupils to select their own methods and instruments of measuring.

Q4 Pupils who need help could be asked for the dimensions of the water tank in centimetres.

Equipment

Three metre sticks, drawing pins, string, long metric tapes, trundle wheel.

UA2b/6
SM4d/6

ME/D1
PFS/E2
ME/E4, 5, 7

Content

- Identification and drawing of cross-sections of prisms
- Area of the cross-section by counting squares
- Volume of a prism by counting cubes and as the Area of cross-section × height.

Introductory activity

Cross-sections
Some discussion, using various solids, may help to identify those which are prisms and the parallel planes which produce identical cross-sections. A useful analogy is to think about how a butcher's slicing machine cuts sausages into 'identical' slices.

Detailed notes

Q1e It is worth discussing that there is a choice of three different cross-sections for a cuboid.

Q2a The faces should be drawn on the grid lines of the squared paper.

Q3a Some pupils may need to be prompted to include those cubes which are hidden in the illustrations.

Q3b The accuracy of the pupils' table should be checked before they attempt Q4.

Additional activity

Designer packaging
Ask pupils to design and construct a box for holding a new brand of chocolate. The box could have a volume of 240 cm^3 and a competition held to find which group designed the most practical, accurate and attractive box. Draw attention to the need for flaps and a lid.

Equipment

Squared paper ($\frac{1}{2}$ or 1 cm).
For the Introductory activity: a variety of solids including a cube, cuboid, cylinder, cone, pyramid, sphere, triangular prism.

A3b/4 → 5
SM4d/6

ME/C3
RS/C1, 3
FE/D1
E+

107	108	109	110	111	112
Revision of language	The probability scale	Calculations	Probability based on statistics	Bias	Combined events

CONTENT AND DEVELOPMENT

Core

Heinemann Mathematics 7 contains work on the language of probability, listing outcomes of events and the use of the probability scale including $0, \frac{1}{2}, 1$.

Heinemann Mathematics 8 covers:

- the language of chance and probability and the use of a probability scale
- calculation of probabilities
- estimation of probabilities based on statistical evidence
- investigation of bias through practical experiments
- identification of all the possible outcomes of two independent combined events
- coded lists and 'tree diagrams'.

National Curriculum (England and Wales)

HD2a, 3acde

Mathematics 5–14 (Scotland)

C/C2
O/C1   **O/D1**   **O/E1**
D/C2
I/C1
RS/D6   **RS/E4**
E+

RELATED ACTIVITIES

What use is probability?
As an investigation into the use of probability in real life, pupils could investigate its use in insurance, weather prediction, or even football pools.

Further work could look at the use of probability in gambling involving games of chance such as roulette and poker. It could be demonstrated that in the long run you are unlikely to benefit from a game that is based on winning through the occurrence of events which have low probabilities.

EQUIPMENT

Scissors, glue, card, 1 cm squared paper, 1 cm and 2 cm isometric dot paper, matchsticks, drawing pins.

For the Introductory activities: Blu-tack, eight prepared shape cards, twelve prepared letter cards.

Content

- Language of chance (no chance/impossible, poor chance, even, good chance, certain)
- Language of probability (0, less than $\frac{1}{2}$, $\frac{1}{2}$, greater than $\frac{1}{2}$, 1)
- Chance and probability on a simple probability scale.

Introductory activity

Using chance and probability
Eight cards could be made as follows: 4 cards each showing a large triangle and 4 cards showing a small rectangle, large rectangle, small circle and large square respectively. The cards can be placed on a flat surface and a pupil, eyes closed or blindfolded, invited to pick one up *at random*. Discuss the *chance* that the card might show a large shape, a small shape, a large triangle, a shape, a pentagon, and position these on a *probability scale*, for example:

Stress the idea of an *even chance* or *evens*. Numerical probabilities 0, less than $\frac{1}{2}$, $\frac{1}{2}$, greater than $\frac{1}{2}$, 1 should be added to the scale.

An alternative approach would be to arrange eight pupils each holding one of the shape cards. A blindfolded pupil is spun around in the middle of the circle and then touches one of the other pupils. Discussion could follow the pattern outlined above, for example, 'What is the chance that the pupil touched has a triangle?' etc.

Pupils might be used without the shapes. For example, 4 without a tie in House A, 1 with and 1 without a tie in House B, 1 without a tie in House C, 1 with a tie in House D.

Equipment

For the Introductory activity: eight prepared shape cards.

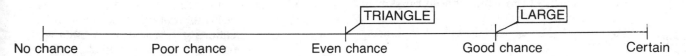

Content

- Calculation of simple probabilities including 0 and 1
- Location of probability on a probability scale.

Introductory activity

Calculating probabilities
Make twelve cards with the letters A, A, A, A, A, A, R, R, R, I, I, U and ask the pupils to discuss the chance that a card picked at random will show the letter R. The letter R has a poor chance of being picked, or probability less than $\frac{1}{2}$. Discussion should then highlight the fact that exact fractional values can be calculated giving more precision. For example, the probability of picking an R is 3 in 12 or $\frac{3}{12}$ or $\frac{1}{4}$.

Emphasise that it is necessary to compare the number of favourable outcomes to the number of possible outcomes. Each probability should then be located on a *probability scale*, for example:

Detailed notes

Panel
after
Q4 — It may be necessary to give further examples of events which have probabilities of 0 or 1.

Equipment

For the Introductory activity: twelve prepared letter cards.

108
Probability:
The
probability
scale

HD3ad/5

E+

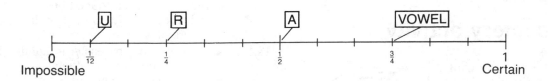

Content

- Calculation of probabilities.

Introductory activity

Fair events
Ask the pupils if any of them have played games such as 'Wheel of Fortune'. Discuss how the games work and whether there is a good or poor chance of winning. It may be possible to work out the probability of winning a prize.

Additional activity

Design an event
Groups could design and construct an event of the type found at a fair. Events shown on Core Textbook page 109 could be used as models. Each group should decide how much to charge players, taking into account the cost of the prizes.

Equipment

None.

110
Probability
based on
statistics

HD2a,
3ac/5

I/C1
O/C1
C/C2
E+

Content

- Interpretation of a bar graph
- Knowledge that repetition of the same experiment may result in different outcomes
- Estimation of probability based on statistical evidence
- Designing an observation sheet to collect data
- Organisation and analysis of survey results.

Organisation

Group organisation is recommended to facilitate discussion among pupils, especially for questions Q4 and Q7.

Detailed notes

Q4 This is the key question on the page. Following pupil discussion in pairs or small groups, class discussion of the pupils' explanations is essential. This discussion should cover points such as:
- a repeat investigation may or may not produce the same results
- results depend wholly and completely on 'the first 100 cars' passing the gates

- Janice's statement might or might not be correct
- a repeat investigation tomorrow or at a different location may or may not produce quite different results
- if frequent repetition of the investigation at different times and locations gave consistent results we *might begin to agree* with Janice.
- even so, any probabilities based on the data would only be *estimates* based on the data collected.

Q7 Pupils should work in groups to design a data collection sheet and to organise the collation of the data. It would be interesting if arrangements could be made for different groups to collect their data on different days or at different times in the day. After the results are analysed they can be discussed on a class basis to see if there is any consistency in them.

Equipment

None.

111
Probability:
Bias

HD3ac/7

O/E1
D/C2
RS/D6
RS/E4
E+

Content

- Construction of frequency tables and bar graphs
- Construction of 3D shapes from nets
- Investigation of bias through practical experiments.

Introductory activity

Loaded die
Construct a die from card with some Blu-tack placed inside it.
Involve the pupils in rolling the die 60 times and recording the results in a frequency table. Using the results, discuss with the class whether the die is 'fair' or not.
The term *bias* could be introduced and discussed.

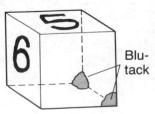

Blu-
tack

Detailed notes

Ex 2 1 cm isometric grid is suitable here.
Ex 2e Discussion might include:
- the symmetry of the spinner would suggest that it is a fair spinner.
- bias may be introduced because of the inaccuracy of the cutting or the positioning of the matchstick.

Ex 3 A larger net may be easier to handle. It could be produced by either
- making edge lengths of 8 cm or
- copying the net onto 2 cm isometric dot paper.

Equipment

Scissors, glue, 1 cm squared paper, card, 1 cm and 2 cm isometric dot paper, matchstick, drawing pin.
For the Introductory activity: Blu-tack.

112
Probability:
Combined
events

HD3e/6

O/D1
O/E1

Content

- Identification of all the possible outcomes of two independent combined events
- Coded lists and 'tree diagrams'.

Equipment

Scissors, card, spent matches (to make spinners).

Introductory activity

Making a systematic list

Revise the use of codes in the systematic creation of lists. For example, 'T-shirts are available in red (r) and blue (b) and in three sizes, Small (S), Medium (M) and Large (L). List all the different T-shirts available.' Possible coded lists might be:

rS, rM, rL, bS, bM, bL

or Sr, Sb, Mr, Mb, Lr, Lb

Introduce an alternative presentation, the 'tree diagram', of these lists. For example:

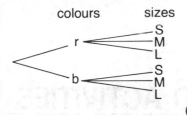

or

6 branches in the tree,
6 different T-shirts.

Alert pupils to the need to leave plenty of vertical space between entries in the first attribute column to allow for the appropriate number of entries in the next column.

Detailed notes

Q4, 1st part Pupils might work in pairs to produce one spinner each.

Q4, 3rd part Class discussion of pupils' answers should highlight that

- the tree has 12 branches; there are 12 possible outcomes
- it is *possible* that 'exactly 12' spins would produce one of each of the 12 possible outcomes
- it is *almost certain* that more than 12 spins will be required.

Q4, 4th part Pupils will need to devise a careful system for recording the outcomes as they occur and the cumulative frequency.

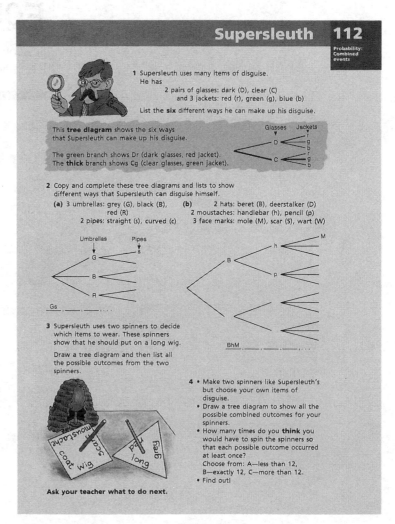

Supersleuth 112

Probability: Combined events

1 Supersleuth uses many items of disguise. He has

2 pairs of glasses: dark (D), clear (C)
and 3 jackets: red (r), green (g), blue (b)

List the **six** different ways he can make up his disguise.

This **tree diagram** shows the six ways that Supersleuth can make up his disguise.

The green branch shows Dr (dark glasses, red jacket).
The **thick** branch shows Cg (clear glasses, green jacket).

2 Copy and complete these tree diagrams and lists to show different ways that Supersleuth can disguise himself.

(a) 3 umbrellas: grey (G), black (B), red (R)
2 pipes: straight (s), curved (c)

(b) 2 hats: beret (B), deerstalker (D)
2 moustaches: handlebar (h), pencil (p)
3 face marks: mole (M), scar (S), wart (W)

3 Supersleuth uses two spinners to decide which items to wear. These spinners show that he should put on a long wig.

Draw a tree diagram and then list all the possible outcomes from the two spinners.

4 • Make two spinners like Supersleuth's but choose your own items of disguise.
• Draw a tree diagram to show all the possible combined outcomes for your spinners.
• How many times do you **think** you would have to spin the spinners so that each possible outcome occurred at least once?
Choose from: A—less than 12, B—exactly 12, C—more than 12.
• Find out!

Ask your teacher what to do next.

113 W15 114 (part)	115 W34	116	117
Make a model	Elimination	Mixed strategies	Mixed strategies

CONTENT AND DEVELOPMENT

Core

Heinemann Mathematics 8, *Problem solving 1* reviews and develops the problem solving strategies Guess and check, Listing systematically and Look for a pattern. A new strategy, Make a table, is introduced and problems requiring the use of a mixture of strategies are provided.

Problem solving 2 introduces two new strategies:

■ Make a model
■ Elimination

A number of problems are also provided which draw on a wide range of problem solving skills and require the use of a mixture of strategies.

As in *Problem solving 1*, it is recommended that the class be organised in groups.

National Curriculum (England and Wales)

UA2abc

Mathematics 5–14 (Scotland)

AS/D
PS/D1   PS/E2
PSE

RELATED ACTIVITIES

Many computer packages are available which set problems in simulated contexts.

EQUIPMENT

Scissors, ruler, 1 mm, $\frac{1}{2}$ cm, 1 cm squared paper, a pack of playing cards.

Content

- Interpretation of information in written and visual forms
- Introduction of the strategy Make a model.

Introductory activity

Crossing the bridge
Discuss the following problem with the class:
Ben has to cross the river using an old rickety bridge. He has with him a bag of corn, a chicken and a dog, of which only one can be carried across at a time. The chicken will eat the corn if left alone with it. The dog will chase the chicken if they are left alone. How can Ben get everything safely across the river?

Class discussion of the problem should include:
- the value of having 'pictures' to aid understanding of problems
- the term 'model', including alternative terms, for example, diagram, chart, sketch.

Detailed notes

Q1a	Pupils could use dots to represent fence posts.
Q1c	Tell pupils that each diagonal plank is 2 m in length.
Q2b	Some pupils may have already produced this design in answer to part (a). They could be asked to design a layout where the four centre squares *do not* all contain a different crop.
Q3	Pupils could act out their solution before recording it.
Q4	It may need to be emphasised that a plank will not reach between stones in neighbouring rows.

Additional activity

Walking the plank
Extend Q4 by asking pupils to find the minimum number of planks needed to cross the river. They may not realise that having used a plank it could be lifted and used again.

Equipment

1 cm or ½ cm squared paper.

113
114
W15
(part)
Problem solving 2:
Make a mode

UA2c/6

PSE

Content

- Interpretation of information in written and visual forms
- Use of the strategies Listing systematically and Make a table
- Introduction of the strategy Elimination.

Introductory activity

Game – Guess that card
Gather together one pupil from each group, 'the leader', and draw a card at random from the pack so that it is known only to the leaders. The leaders return to the groups who try to guess the card, keeping a note of the questions asked and the total number of questions needed to identify the card.

Discuss with the class which are the best questions to ask – those which will *eliminate* the greatest number of possibilities at one time. For example: 'Is it red?' rather than 'Is it the three of hearts?'

Repeat the activity for different cards. Discuss the set of 'best' questions.

Detailed notes

W34, Q2b	Different answers are possible depending on the clue made up by the pupil. For example: 'It contains a vowel' or 'It contains a P'.
W34, Q3	Help is provided to enable pupils to draw up a systematic list in preparation for Q4 and Q5 on Core Textbook page 115, where help is *not* given. Nevertheless, some pupils may need assistance to begin the listing required in the Core Textbook questions.
W34, Q5, Q6	The pupil is helped to form an attribute table in preparation for the challenge Q7 on Core Textbook page 115.

Equipment

For the Introductory activity: a pack of playing cards.

115
W34
Problem solving 2:
Elimination

UA2c/6

PSE

116

Problem
solving 2:
Mixed
strategies

UA2b/6

AS/D
PSE

Content

- Interpretation of information in written and visual forms
- Use of the strategies Make a model, Reasoning and Elimination.

Detailed notes

Q1c Pupils having difficulty may find it helpful to cut out and experiment with 8 pieces of paper each showing the number of passengers in a group.

Q2 Pupils could make a model by using strips of paper cut to a scale of 1 cm to 1 m, for example:

Ford Pop	Model Y	Funny Car

Equipment
Scissors, ruler.

117

Problem
solving 2:
Mixed
Strategies

UA2a/6

PS/D
PS/E2
PSE

Content

- Interpretation of information in written and visual forms
- Use of the strategies Make a table, Looking for a pattern, Listing systematically and Reasoning.

Detailed notes

Q5, 6 Pupils are intended to realise that these questions pose essentially the same problem as in Q1–Q4, although they are presented in a different form. On/off has become open/shut and down/up.

Q7 Most pupils are likely to adopt a Make a model strategy. Some able pupils may link the problem with Q1 and reason logically on the basis of results achieved there. For example, 3 ways of having 2 lights on in the top row, similarly for the bottom row, giving $3 \times 3 = 9$ ways. Add 3 ways of having 3 lights on in the top row, similarly for the bottom row, giving $3 + 3 = 6$.

Grand total $9 + 6 = 15$ ways.

As an alternative, Listing systematically could be used to show all possible positions of the two lights.

Equipment
None.

DETOURS IN PART 3

*General advice about using the Detours can be found
on page T6 of these Notes.*

87
88
Detour:
Investigating
networks

UA3ab/6

FE/E4
PSE

Content

- Interpretation of information in written and visual form
- Use of networks to solve problems.

Pupils work systematically to investigate the rules for drawing networks.

Organisation

Two or more pupils could cooperate to obtain the data for all the networks. Group discussion would be valuable in finding the general principles concerning the traversability of networks including the possible start and finish points.

Introductory activity

The rules
Challenge pupils to draw these shapes according to the rules.

possible   impossible

Ask them to demonstrate their solutions before beginning the work of the page.

Detailed notes

Q2d The pupils should realise that even-junction networks can be drawn starting and finishing at the same junction.

Q5a There are many different possible routes since all the junctions are even.

Q5b Ash Avenue/Beech Glade and Ash Avenue/Elms Way become the only two odd junctions.

Additional activity

Delivery routes
Pupils could draw sketch maps of their local streets and suggest optimum newspaper or milk delivery runs designed if possible to involve travelling along the streets once only.

Equipment
None.

Content

- Rounding to the nearest 100 and 1000
- Use of rounded numbers to find mentally approximate sums and differences
- Use of multiplication to check answers to division
- Interpretation of calculator displays which have rounding errors.

102
Detour:
Checking
answers

N3ef,
4c/4 → 5

I/E5
AS/D1
MD/D4
RN/D1

Detailed notes

Panel above Q1, 2nd to last line Emphasise that one way to check whether a calculator answer is 'reasonable' is to calculate mentally an approximate answer.

Panel beside Q4b It would be helpful to have available for discussion and demonstration a calculator which does *not* have this have type of 'rounding' error.

Equipment
Calculator.

S36

Detour:
Shape
through
pattern

A2b/4
SM2a/4

S/D2

Content

- Interpretation of information in written and visual form.

In this practical activity pupils work methodically to construct a cardioid from straight lines.

Additional activity

More patterns

Pupils could investigate shapes produced using other rules, for example

- $1 \longrightarrow 20, 2 \longrightarrow 21, 3 \longrightarrow 22, \ldots$, which gives a circle
- $1 \longrightarrow 3, 2 \longrightarrow 6, 3 \longrightarrow 9, 4 \longrightarrow 12, \ldots$, which gives a kidney shape or nephroid.

As this requires working round the circumference three times some pupils may find it helpful to continue the numbering to 216.

Equipment

Ruler, sharp pencil.
For the Additional activity: extra copies of page S36.

Content

- Interpretation of information in written and visual form.

Pupils work systematically to predict within given rules the least number of colours needed to colour any map.

Detailed notes

Panel above Q1 It may be necessary to clarify the colouring rules by further explanation and examples.

Q1 Emphasise that pupils are to use as *few* colours as possible.

Q2 Ask pupils to include in their designs maps which require four colours.

Q3 It could be suggested to pupils that they *try* to design a map requiring five colours.

Equipment

Coloured pencils.

E20
E21

Detour:
Translation
and reflection

SM2c,3c/5

S/D1, 2
S/E2
PM/D4

Content

- Interpretation of information in written and visual form
- Construction of patterns by repeated transformations of an original shape.

The transformations are translation, reflection and combined translation and reflection.

Organisation

The pupils should investigate the construction of patterns individually or in pairs. Little or no teacher help is envisaged. The patterns produced should be colourful and attractive and could be used for a wall display.

Equipment

Tracing paper, $\frac{1}{2}$ cm squared paper, coloured pencils.

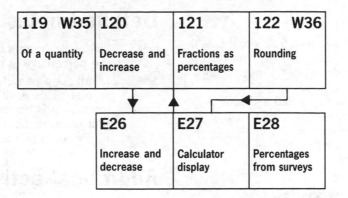

119 W35	120	121	122 W36
Of a quantity	Decrease and increase	Fractions as percentages	Rounding

E26	E27	E28
Increase and decrease	Calculator display	Percentages from surveys

CONTENT AND DEVELOPMENT

Core

Heinemann Mathematics 8 *Percentages 1* revises and develops the concept of per cent, common percentages as simple fractions and calculations based on 10% and 1%. The calculator is *not* used.

Throughout *Percentages 2* **a calculator is used**. The section covers:

- calculation of percentages of a quantity
- construction and interpretation of percentage pie charts
- percentage increase and decrease
- expressing one quantity as a percentage of another
- expressing a fraction as a percentage
- rounding to the nearest whole number and hundredth
- collection, organisation, display and interpretation of survey data.

Not all calculators work in the manner shown. It is worth checking that pupils are confident in the use of individual calculators.

Extension

E26 extends the work of Core Textbook page 120 and contains work on the direct method of calculating percentage increase or decrease.

E27 and E28 should be attempted on completion of Core Textbook page 122.

National Curriculum (England and Wales)

N2b, 3cdf
HD2abf

Mathematics 5–14 (Scotland)

PSE	C/E2	D/D1	D/E2	D/E
I/D1	I/E1	RTN/D3, 4	AS/D3	
FPR/E2	RN/D1	E+		

RELATED ACTIVITIES

Percentage change
Encourage pupils to collect examples of percentage changes illustrating the wide range of language associated with percentage increase and decrease. Shops, magazines, newspapers, advertisements, leaflets, labels, empty cartons and so on provide many examples. Selected items could be displayed to stimulate interest and give realism and motivation to this work.

EQUIPMENT

Calculator, $\frac{1}{2}$ cm squared paper, coloured pencils.

For the Introductory activities: newspaper/magazine article, item displaying percentage increase/decrease.

119
W35
ercentages 2:
Of a quantity

N2b, 3c/5
HD2f/5

D/D1
I/D1
I/E1
RTN/D3, 4
FPR/E2

Content

- Meaning of percentage as a fraction and as a decimal
- Calculation of percentages of a quantity by calculator
  - using percentages expressed as decimals
  - using the percentage key
- Interpretation of percentage pie charts
- Construction and interpretation of a combined bar graph.

Introductory activity

Using a calculator for percentage work
A newspaper or magazine article, using percentages to report the results of a survey on a topical issue, might be used to

- revise the meaning of percentage as hundredths and in decimal form, for example:
  45%   45 hundredths   0·45
- revise calculation of percentages of a quantity by entering the percentage as a two-place decimal, for example:
  45% of 540 entered as

  [0] [·] [4] [5] [×] [5] [4] [0] [=]

- introduce the use of the percentage key, for example:
  45% of 540 entered as

  [5] [4] [0] [×] [4] [5] [%]

  One explanation might be: 45% of 540 can be regarded as 45% × 540 and since multiplication is commutative this is the same as 540 × 45%.

Note: Not all calculators use the percentage key in this way. The method taught should be appropriate for the calculators available.

Detailed notes

Q4c Although the number of men is greater, the percentage of men is smaller.

Q4d Lentil soup was chosen by 60 men and 60 women. This is 40% of men and 48% of women. It is important to discuss the fact that equal numbers do not necessarily imply equal percentages.

Additional activity

Class favourite soup survey
Pupils could conduct their own class survey and the results compared with the Slimma Soups surveys. Many follow-up questions could be asked, for example:

- is lentil the favourite?
- is the same favourite chosen by boys and girls?

Equipment

Calculator, $\frac{1}{2}$ cm squared paper.
For the Introductory activity: newspaper/magazine article.

120
ercentages 2:
Decrease and
increase

N2b, 3c/6

RTN/D4
AS/D3
FPR/E2

Content

- Percentage decrease and increase and associated language.

Introductory activity

Language
Terms which can be used in each type of problem should be discussed. In particular, for problems involving
subtraction: decrease, less, discount, off, reduction
addition: increase, more, extra, bigger.
Other words which could arise include longer, shorter, rise, fall and so on.

Additional activity

10% bigger bars
Have an item available which is clearly labelled '10% bigger', or similar, for example a bar of chocolate, newspaper advert and so on. An explanation of '10% bigger' is likely to appear on the item, for example '165 g for the price of 150 g'. The discussion should highlight

- the original size was 150 g
- the increase is 10% of 150 g = 15 g
- the new size is 150 + 15 = 165 g.

Equipment

Calculator.
For the Additional activity: item displaying percentage increase or decrease.

Content

- Conversion of fractions to decimals and percentages
- Expressing one quantity as a percentage of another.

Introductory activity

Youth Club
The Youth Club data shown opposite could be used to express one quantity as a fraction and then as a percentage of another.

Youth Club
Boys 27
Girls 33
Can swim – 18 boys
27 girls

For example:
The fraction of members who are boys is
27 out of 60 or $\frac{27}{60}$.
This can be expressed in percentage form by finding
$27 \div 60 = 0\cdot45 = 45\%$
The percentage can be checked by using equivalence
$\frac{27}{60} = \frac{9}{20} = \frac{45}{100} = 45\%$
This can be repeated for
- the fraction of members who can swim
- the fraction of swimmers who are boys.

Detailed notes

121
Percentages
Fractions as
percentages

N2b, 3d/6

RTN/D3, 4

| Panel above Q1 | The use of the % key in the second to last line should be discussed. |
| Q3 | Pupils should check that the answers to (a) and (b) total 100%. |

Equipment

Calculator.

Content

- Expressing one quantity as a percentage of another
- Rounding to the nearest whole number or hundredth
- Construction and interpretation of pie charts
- Collection, organisation, display and interpretation of survey data.

Organisation

Q7 requires pupils to work in groups to conduct a survey.

Introductory activity

Our class
The Introductory activity described for Core Textbook page 121 could be repeated using data collected for the class. This should result in the need to round the calculator display. Both situations, rounding to the nearest whole number and to the nearest hundredth, should be discussed.

Detailed notes

122
W36
Percentages
Rounding

N2b, 3d/6

PSE
C/E2
D/E2
I/D1
RTN/D3, 4
RN/D1
E+

Q5	Use of coloured pencils should improve the visual impact of the pie charts.
Q6	From the results pupils could be asked to describe the holiday which is likely to appeal to a large number of people.
Q7	Encourage pupils to make up their own questions. Their results could be reported to others in a class discussion.

Equipment

Calculator, coloured pencils.

E26

centages 2:
ncrease and
decrease

N2b, 3d/6

RTN/D4
FPR/E2

Content

■ Direct calculation of new prices given percentage increase or reduction.

Introductory activity

Price increase
Discuss situations of the type shown below where there are percentage increases.

Sweatshirt	£22	Increase	15%
Sports bag	£16	Increase	7%
Boots	£64	Increase	21%

The new price of the sweatshirt could first be found indirectly as before. The direct method illustrated in the panel at the top of E26 should then be explained.

Detailed notes

Panel above Q2	If necessary a similar approach to the Introductory activity could be taken.
Q2	Pupils must determine the category of each item in order to use the appropriate percentage reduction.

Equipment

Calculator.

E27

rcentages 2:
Calculator
display

**N2b,
3df/6**

PSE
C/E2
RTN/D3, 4
RN/D1
E+

Content

■ Interpretation of information from a television programme schedule
■ Expressing one quantity as a percentage of another by calculator
■ Rounding to the nearest whole number or hundredth
■ Collection, organisation and display of survey data.

Organisation

Q7 requires pupils to work as a group to plan and carry out a survey for a television channel.

Detailed notes

Panel above Q2	This assumes the 'afternoon' programmes to last from 12.00 to 6.00.
Q4b	Pupils should realise that all three sports programmes have to be totalled.

Equipment

Calculator.

E28
Percentages
Percentages
from surveys

N2b, 3d/6
HD2ab/5

PSE
C/E2
D/D1
D/E
I/D1
RTN/D3, 4
RN/D1
FPR/E2
E+

Content

- Interpretation of a bar graph showing data from a survey
- Expressing a fraction as a percentage
- Rounding to the nearest whole number or hundredth
- Calculation of a percentage of a quantity
- Selection and construction of the most appropriate graph to illustrate data
- Collection, organisation, display and interpretation of survey data.

Equipment

Calculator.

Organisation

Groups are required for Q7 and Q8.
Q8 asks for a survey to be carried out.

Detailed notes

Q1b There should be discussion of the different explanations suggested.

Q3 The answers can be obtained using either the percentages shown in the graph or the fractions obtained in Q2.

Q7 A variety of graphs should be produced. Examples include bar graphs, pie charts and trend graphs.

Q8 There is no need for the survey to be about smoking. Alternative surveys should be suggested by the pupils, for example:

- taste in music
- favourite sports or hobbies.

Encourage pupils to comment on their results, for example, describe trends, suggest reasons for any trends and so on.

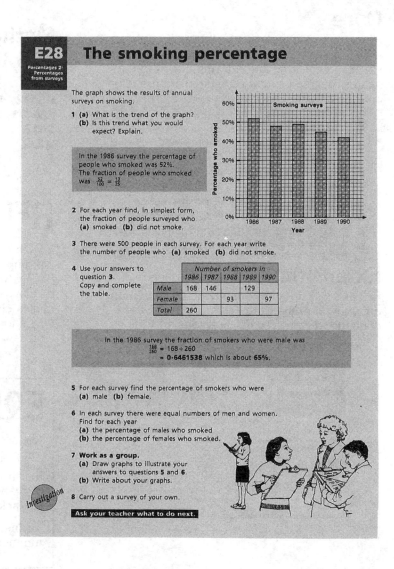

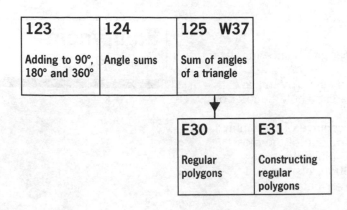

123	124	125 W37
Adding to 90°, 180° and 360°	Angle sums	Sum of angles of a triangle

E30	E31
Regular polygons	Constructing regular polygons

CONTENT AND DEVELOPMENT

Core

Heinemann Mathematics 8, *Angles 1*, contains work on angle terminology, naming angles and shapes, measuring and drawing angles to the nearest degree using a semi-circular protractor and three-figure bearings.

Angles 2, covers:

- the terms port and starboard and the use of three-figure bearings
- calculation of angles whose sum is 90°, 180°, 360°
- meaning of vertically opposite angles
- measurement of angles to the nearest degree
- sum of the angles forming a straight line
- sum of the angles of a triangle.

Extension

E30 and E31 should normally be attempted on completion of the Core Textbook pages and contains work on regular polygons, including:

- the meaning of a regular polygon and calculation of the angle subtended at the centre by a side
- construction of regular polygons.

National Curriculum (England and Wales)

SM2bcd, 3d

Mathematics 5–14 (Scotland)

PSE
RS/D2, 4
PM/D1, 2
S/D2   S/E1
A/D2   A/E2, 4   A/E
E+

RELATED ACTIVITIES

Angles in use
Ask pupils to collect pictures, logos, designs or badges which show angles and polygons. A wall display of the collection could be made and angles clearly marked and labelled with size and type and the different types of polygons named.

EQUIPMENT

Protractor, plain paper, ruler, tracing paper, compasses, coloured pencils, 50p coin.

For an Introductory activity: 3 strips of Meccano *or* card and paper fastener *or* string, Blu-tack, metre stick.

For the Additional activities: coloured gummed paper, coin or circular object.

ANGLES 2

114

Content

- Use of port and starboard to indicate the direction of a rotation
- Informal calculation of complementary, supplementary and reflex angles using three-figure bearings.

Introductory activity

Port and starboard
The four main compass points could be drawn on the floor and a pupil, standing in the centre with outstretched arm, could demonstrate turning on the spot through 90°, 180°, 270°, 360° to port or starboard. The activity could be extended by using different starting positions, for example NE, 315° or 050°.

A way to connect 'left' and 'port' is to remember that they have the same number of letters.

Detailed notes

Q2 If necessary, remind pupils that for each part of this question the *Queen Bess* starts in the original position shown in the illustration.

Q4 Pupils should answer all five parts for *Saucy Sue* before moving to *Skylark* and so on.

Q5b It may help some pupils to make a sketch of the return journey with the arrows in the opposite direction and with the lines on each section of the course extended.

Additional activity

Plotting a course
Pupils could draw their own courses which could have more than two turns and ask neighbours to fully describe the turns necessary to negotiate the courses.

The use of a software package incorporating Logo commands could provide consolidation of the ideas contained on this page.

Equipment

None.

123
Angles 2:
Adding to 90°
180° and 360°

SM2d/
5 → 6

PM/D1, 2
A/D2

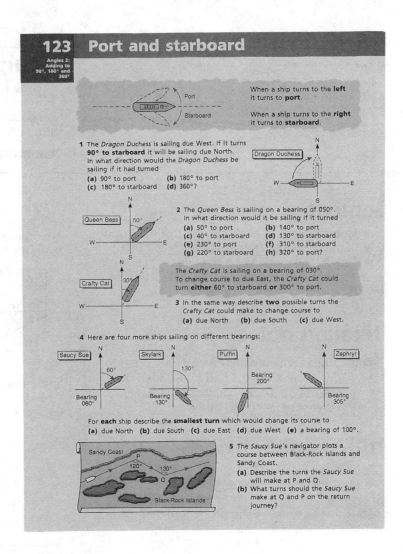

124
Angles 2:
Angle sums

SM2d/6

A/E2

A/E

Content

- Calculation of angles whose sum is 90°, 180°, 360°
- Meaning of vertically opposite angles.

Introductory activity

The other angle
Any of the materials shown could be used in a discussion in which pupils are given the size of one angle and asked to find the other.

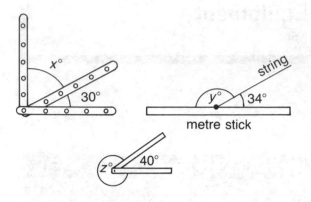
metre stick

Detailed notes

Q1 It may be necessary to emphasise that the pupils should not try to measure the angles but should calculate them.

Q2b Pupils should estimate before measuring to help avoid errors such as reading from the wrong scale.

Additional activity

Vertically opposite angles
Tracing paper could be used to verify that vertically opposite angles are equal. A more formal proof could also be considered:

$$r + q = 180$$
$$r + s = 180$$

Hence $q = s$.

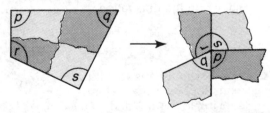

Equipment

Protractor.
For the Introductory activity: 3 strips of Meccano *or* card and paper fastener *or* string, Blu-tack, metre stick.

125
W37
Angles 2:
um of angles
of a triangle

SM2d/6

PSE

A/E

A/E4

Content

- Measurement of angles to the nearest degree
- Sum of the angles forming a straight line
- Sum of the angles of a triangle.

An investigation of the angle-sum by considering several different types of triangle.

Detailed notes

W37, Q2c When individual angles are measured to the nearest degree and then added the total may not be exactly 180°. Answers may vary by 2 or 3 degrees.

Additional activities

1 Sum of the angles of a triangle
Give pupils a triangular piece of coloured gummed paper and ask them to mark the angles as shown. The corners should be torn and placed next to each other to form a straight angle.

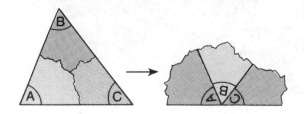

2 Sum of angles of a quadrilateral
Ask pupils to find the sum of the angles of a quadrilateral by tearing off the corners and fitting them together.

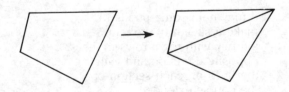

Some pupils may be able to deduce the result directly using a diagram such as this one and their knowledge of the angle-sum for a triangle.

Equipment

Protractor, plain paper, ruler.
For the Additional activities: coloured gummed paper.

Content

- Meaning of polygon and regular polygon
- Calculation of the angle at the centre of a regular polygon subtended by a side.

Introductory activity

Naming polygons
There could be some discussion of the numbers associated with the prefixes tri, quad, penta, hexa, . . ., and poly. Ask pupils to suggest words with these prefixes and discuss their meaning. Likely suggestions are triangle, tricycle, tripod, quadruplets, quadrilateral, quadrangle, pentathlon, the Pentagon, octet, octogenarian, polytechnic, polygamy and so on.

Pupils could also be asked to invent names for other polygons with, for example, a hundred sides ('centagon').

Detailed notes

Q2b There is an opportunity here to introduce the formal language 'centre of rotational symmetry'.

Panel above Q3, last line Pupils can confirm that the angles are equal by tracing the diagram and rotating the tracing.

Additional activity

Nuts and bolts
Most nuts and boltheads are hexagonal. Ask pupils to suggest why this shape is chosen. Suggestions might include:

- the spanner can fit in several ways, which is useful if access is limited.
- the fewer the number of sides, the longer the side length, hence a good grip can be made and the spanner is less likely to slip.

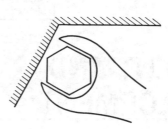

Equipment

Tracing paper.

Content

- Construction of a regular polygon by drawing equal angles at the centre of a circle
- Construction of a regular curvilinear heptagon
- Investigation of methods for accurately constructing an enlargement of the shape of a 50p coin.

Detailed notes

Q4 A wall display could be made using pupils' coloured designs.

Q5 This challenge may be tackled in either of these ways.
- Draw the angles at the centre and mark the seven points on the circumference. Using radius and centre shown draw a curve.
Do this seven times.

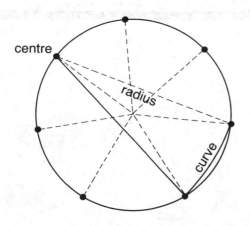

- Draw round a 50p piece. Draw an enlargement using a dilatation.

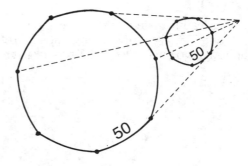

SM2bd/6;
3d/6

PSE
RS/D2, 4
S/D2
A/E
E+

Additional activities

1 Penny hexagon
Using a coin or any circular object, pupils could construct a hexagon as shown.

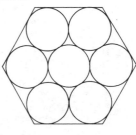

2 Design a coin
Pupils could design their own coin in the shape of a curvilinear pentagon or nonagon.

A wall display of the designs could be made.

Equipment

Compasses, protractor, coloured pencils, 50p coin.
For Additional activity 1: coin or circular object.

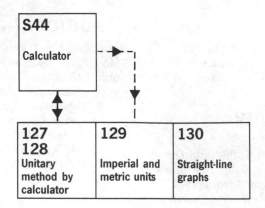

S44		
Calculator		

127 128	129	130
Unitary method by calculator	Imperial and metric units	Straight-line graphs

CONTENT AND DEVELOPMENT

Core

In Heinemann Mathematics 8, *Proportion 1* develops, using paper and pencil calculations, the unitary method of proportion, the 'multiple' method and comparative costs to find the 'best buy'.

In *Proportion 2* the work is extended to include:

- the unitary method using a calculator
- interpretation of straight-line conversion graphs
- construction and interpretation of straight-line graphs representing two quantities in direct proportion.

Support

S44 provides lead-in material to Core Textbook pages 127 and 128. Alternatively, on completion of S44, pupils may go directly to Core Textbook page 129.

National Curriculum (England and Wales)

N3c, 4a
SM4a
HD2f

Mathematics 5–14 (Scotland)

PSE   D/E1   I/D1   MD/D4   MD/E
RN/D1   ME/D9   E+

RELATED ACTIVITIES

Material is available containing information about quantities in proportion. For example, garages are able to supply ready reckoners and/or graphs of petrol costs and gallons/litres conversion. Travel agents, banks and building societies have information in similar forms on foreign exchange rates.

This material could provide a basis for general discussion about the concept of direct proportion and graph work.

EQUIPMENT

Computer, $\frac{1}{2}$ cm squared paper, timer (seconds not necessary), novel, calculator.

Content

- Interpretation of information in written form
- Direct proportion by the unitary method using a calculator
- Approximation to the nearest unit, ten or other appropriate degree of accuracy
- Use of the problem solving strategies Reasoning, Working backwards, Elimination, Trial and improvement.

Introductory activity

Fruit punch
Discuss how to increase the quantities in this recipe to make sufficient punch to give all the pupils in the class one glass each.

Recipe
1 carton   (200 ml) Orange juice
2 cartons (400 ml) Apple juice
3 cartons (600 ml) Pineapple juice
(Makes 8 glasses)

The method of recording shown in the panel on Core Textbook page 127 should be used in the calculations. The calculator displays will need careful discussion and should be rounded to give the quantities correct to the nearest carton.

Detailed notes

Slush panel above Q1, 2nd to last line The efficient use of the calculator is shown. Pupils using this method need not record the answer to the division. In this case the tabular layout shown for the truffles recipe may be considered appropriate.

Q3 Discuss the rounding used by the pupils after they have attempted the question. Eggs clearly need to be rounded to the nearest unit; other ingredients could be rounded to the nearest 10.

Q5 Ask pupils to work in groups to consider possible solutions. Flour is the key limiting ingredient.

Additional activities

1 Class party
Based on Q1 to Q4, calculate the cost of a class party. How much food and drink should be provided? What must be bought and how much will it cost?

2 Additional recipes
The Home Economics department or the library should be able to supply recipes which may be adapted in a similar way to those on the page.

Equipment

Calculator.

127 128
Proportion 2: Unitary method by calculator

N3c, 4a/5

PSE
MD/D4
MD/E
RN/D1

Content

- Imperial units (1 oz, 1 pt) and their rough metric equivalents (30 g, 570 ml)
- Interpretation of straight-line conversion graphs.

Introductory activity

Metric and Imperial units
The scene could be set by discussing metric and Imperial units with the emphasis on weight and volume. Some items are marked in both metric and Imperial units (potatoes, milk), indeed some shopkeepers still weigh in pounds and ounces. Ask pupils to examine the recipe for Granny Jessie's soup and to suggest how it differs from the recipes illustrated on Core Textbook pages 127 and 128. The graphs could be discussed, paying attention to the scales used and the conversions illustrated.

Additional activities

1 Recipes
Pupils could find other recipes written in Imperial units and use graphs to convert the quantities to metric units.

2 Display of units
Pupils could collect cartons, boxes, bottles, labels and so on which show Imperial and/or metric units. These could be displayed in the classroom.

Equipment

None.

129
Proportion 2: Imperial and metric units

SM4a/5
HD2f/5

I/D1
ME/D9

130
Proportion 2:
Straight-line
graphs

N3c/5
HD2f/5

I/D1
D/E1
E+

Content

- Construction and interpretation of straight-line graphs representing two quantities in direct proportion
- Concept and language of 'in proportion'.

Organisation

For Q8 each pupil needs access to a microcomputer for about five minutes. If the number of pupils is large and/or access to microcomputers is limited, the practical work may have to be spread over more than one lesson. Some pupils may have access to a microcomputer out of school which could be used for the practical work.

Introductory activity

How quickly can you type?
Discuss the nature of the work of the page. The pupils are going to draw graphs of their own typing times and compare them with those of Amir and Helen.

Detailed notes

Panel above Q8 Discuss the statements in the panel in relation to Amir and Helen's graphs, for example:
- the two quantities (time, number of lines) are related
- if one doubles/halves, is multiplied/divided by 3 and so on, then so is the other.
- the two quantities are said to be in proportion
- when two quantities in proportion in this way are graphed the graph is a straight line through the origin.

Q8 The pupils could first estimate how long they would take to type the 48 lines.

Equipment

Computer, $\frac{1}{2}$ cm squared paper, timer (seconds not necessary), novel, calculator.

Content

- Direct proportion by the unitary method using a calculator
- Interpretation of information in visual and written form
- Division and multiplication of money by two-digit whole numbers.

Introductory activity

Use of the calculator
Demonstrate the use of the calculator as indicated in the panel at the top of S44. Particular attention should be paid to the interpretation of the display as representing amounts of money at each stage of the calculation.

Detailed notes

Q1 Pupils should realise that the first entry into the calculator is the given cost.

Equipment

Calculator.

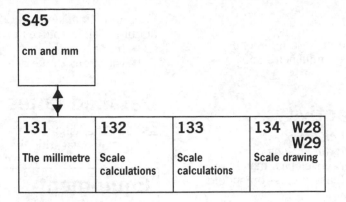

CONTENT AND DEVELOPMENT

Core

Heinemann Mathematics 7 contains work on the millimetre, scale calculations and scale drawing.

Heinemann Mathematics 8 develops and consolidates these and includes

- measurement to the nearest millimetre
- relationship among metres, centimetres and millimetres
- introduction of scale in ratio form
- finding a scale
- use of scale to calculate plan and true lengths
- construction of scale drawings.

Support

S45 provides lead-in material to Core Textbook page 131.

National Curriculum (England & Wales)

UA2c
N2b, 3c
SM3d, 4ab

Mathematics 5–14 (Scotland)

RTN/D4
FPR/E5
ME/D1
PFS/E3

RELATED ACTIVITIES

Use furniture catalogues to plan and cost fitted bedrooms, kitchens, and so on.

EQUIPMENT

Ruler, scissors, glue or sticky tape, 1 mm or 2 mm squared paper, calculator.

For the Introductory activities: sheets of paper, envelopes, matchboxes, chalk boxes or similar, brochures containing house plans.

For the Additional activities: long metric tape, callipers, 1 cm squared paper, furniture catalogues.

For the Related activity: furniture catalogues.

131
Length and scale:
The millimetre

SM4ab/5

RTN/D4
ME/D1

Content

- Measurement to the nearest millimetre
- Relationship between millimetre and centimetre.

Introductory activity

Measuring to the nearest millimetre
Pupils could measure the dimensions of, for example, sheets of paper, envelopes, matchboxes, chalk boxes and so on. Class discussion should stress

- that measuring starts at 0
- 10 mm = 1 cm
- the different recording methods, for example, 43 mm *or* 4 cm 3 mm *or* 4·3 cm.

Variations in answers should lead to discussion about possible sources of inaccuracy such as

- human error
- variations in the actual rulers.

Detailed notes

Q2 The lengths of the shells should be found by measuring the thin horizontal lines.

Equipment

Ruler.
For the Introductory activity: sheets of paper, envelopes, matchboxes, chalk boxes or similar.

132
Length and scale:
Scale calculations

SM3d,
4a/5

RTN/D4
ME/D1
PFS/E3

Content

- Measurement to the nearest millimetre
- Relationship among metres, centimetres and millimetres
- Calculation of true lengths using scales of the type 1 cm to x cm and 1 cm to x m.

Detailed notes

Panel above Q1 Interpretation of scale drawing may need to be revised, emphasising that the method for calculating true lengths involves

- measuring
- multiplying
- converting to the appropriate units.

Q2 whale The scale of the whale drawing is different from the others. Some pupils may realise that it is easier to answer part (b) before part (a).

Q3 Pupils may again need help with the whale. The scale should first be converted to 1 cm to 300 cm.

Additional activity

Scale models
Pupils could find the true sizes from model cars, ships, planes, trains and so on. Pupils are likely to discover that scales can be expressed in a variety of forms which may require some explanation. This activity could lead to discussion about methods of measuring these models. One method is shown below. Callipers may also be used.

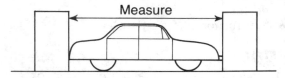

Measure

Equipment

For the Additional activity: ruler, calculator, callipers.

133
Length and scale:
Scale calculations

SM3d/5

RTN/D4
FPR/E5
ME/D1
PFS/E3

Content

- Measurement to the nearest millimetre
- Introduction of scale in ratio form and calculation of true lengths
- Finding a scale.

Introductory activity

House plans
Brochures from estate agents, builders and show houses containing scale drawings of houses could be discussed. Particular emphasis should be placed on the meaning of the new ratio notation.

Alternatively, plans may be borrowed from the school's technology department. Scale drawings of the school building may also be available.

Detailed notes

Q1 Some pupils may find it helpful to complete the length column in the table before calculating the true lengths.

Q2 It may be helpful to discuss the connection between the floor plan and the scale drawing in Q1.
Pupils could be advised to use the longer side as the 'length' of a room.

Additional activity

Classroom plan
Pupils could measure the dimensions of the classroom and using the same scale 1:40 draw its plan.

Equipment

Ruler.
For the Introductory activity: brochures containing house plans.
For the Additional activity: long metric tape, 1 cm squared paper (A4).

Content

- Use of scale to calculate plan and true lengths
- Construction of scale drawings

The work involves planning furniture layouts.

Organisation

Pupils could work in small groups to allow discussion and share equipment. Measurements for Q3 need to be taken at the pupil's home.

Introductory activity

The classroom
Discuss reasons for the positions of various items of classroom furniture, for example, to avoid blocking passageways, to allow access, to ensure sunlight and so on.

Detailed notes

Q1 Explain that this bedroom is the same one as in the plan on Core Textbook page 133.

Q1b Pupils are expected to take into account the positions of the windows and door.

Q2 Pupils may be confused about length and breadth as the room is L-shaped.

Additional activity

Costing the plans
Catalogues could be used to plan and cost fitted bedrooms, kitchens and so on.

Equipment

Ruler, scissors, glue or sticky tape, 1 mm or 2 mm squared paper.
For the Additional activity: furniture catalogues.

134
W28
W29
Length and scale:
Scale drawing

UA2c/6
N2b, 3c/6
SM3d/6

ME/D1
FPR/E5
PFS/E3

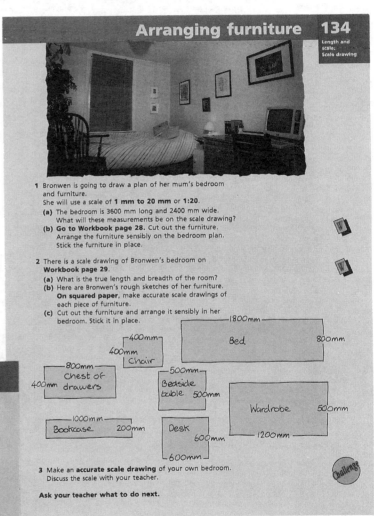

Arranging furniture 134
Length and scale:
Scale drawing

1 Bronwen is going to draw a plan of her mum's bedroom and furniture.
She will use a scale of **1 mm to 20 mm** or **1:20**.
   (a) The bedroom is 3600 mm long and 2400 mm wide. What will these measurements be on the scale drawing?
   (b) **Go to Workbook page 28.** Cut out the furniture. Arrange the furniture sensibly on the bedroom plan. Stick the furniture in place.

2 There is a scale drawing of Bronwen's bedroom on **Workbook page 29.**
   (a) What is the true length and breadth of the room?
   (b) Here are Bronwen's rough sketches of her furniture. **On squared paper**, make accurate scale drawings of each piece of furniture.
   (c) Cut out the furniture and arrange it sensibly in her bedroom. Stick it in place.

3 Make an **accurate scale drawing** of your own bedroom. Discuss the scale with your teacher.

Ask your teacher what to do next.

Bronwen's bedroom 29

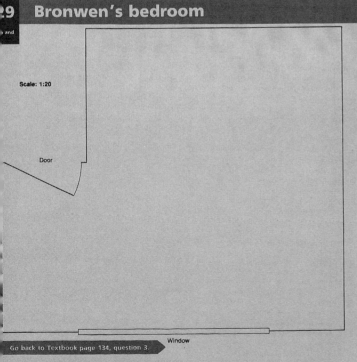

Scale: 1:20

Door

Window

Go back to Textbook page 134, question 3.

S45
Length and
scale:
cm and mm

SM3d,
4a/5

RTN/D4
ME/D1

Content

- Measurement to the nearest millimetre
- Relationship between millimetre and centimetre.

Introductory activity

Measuring to the nearest millimetre
Details are provided in the Introductory activity for Core Textbook page 131.

Detailed notes

Panel above Q1 It may be necessary to discuss how these lengths have been obtained by measuring the diagram of the Lotus 72.

In particular it should be noted that:
- measuring starts at 0
- 10 mm = 1 cm
- 67 mm = 6 cm 7 mm = 6·7 cm

Q2 The pupils may need to be shown that the height of each car is measured from the line on which the wheels rest to the highest point.

Equipment
Ruler.

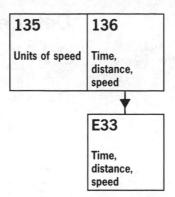

135	136
Units of speed	Time, distance, speed

↓

E33
Time, distance, speed

CONTENT AND DEVELOPMENT

Core

In Heinemann Mathematics 7, speed (m/s, km/h, mph) is included as a particular example of a rate.

Heinemann Mathematics 8 consolidates and extends earlier work and covers:

- informal calculation of speed in m/s and km/h
- mental calculation of distance, given time and speed in km/h and mph.

Extension

E33 should be attempted following completion of Core Textbook page 136. It extends the work of the Core Textbook to include calculation of time given distance and speed in km/h.

National Curriculum (England and Wales)

SM4c

Mathematics 5–14 (Scotland)

MD/D1   **MD/E1**   **MD/E**
RN/D1
ME/D1
T/D1, 2
PFS/E3
E+

EQUIPMENT

Calculator, ruler.

For an Additional activity: map showing distances between towns.

SM4c/7

MD/D1
MD/E
RN/D1
E+

Content

- Informal calculation of speed in m/s and km/h
- Rounding a calculator display to the nearest whole number.

Introductory activity

Speed
Discuss the concept of speed using a simple example of the type 'Jasmine drives 100 kilometres in 2 hours. What is the average speed for her journey?' Discussion of further similar examples may be necessary for some pupils.

Detailed notes

| Panel above Q3 | Additional practice in converting minutes and seconds to seconds and in rounding may be required. |

| Q5 | Some pupils may have difficulty because of the variety of units and the different ways in which the data is presented. |

Equipment

Calculator.

SM4c/7

MD/D1
MD/E1
T/D1, 2
E+

Content

- Mental calculation of distance, given time and speed
- Interpretation of information in written and visual form.

Detailed notes

| Q5 | This is possibly best answered by looking at the table in Q2. In 4 hours from 9 am till 13.00 they travel about 280 km. |

| Q8 | 'Just over 2 hours' would be an acceptable answer. Able pupils should be expected to give the answer as 'about 2 hours 12 minutes'. |

| Q9 | One approach is to find how far they can travel in the three-and-a-half hours to midnight. |

Additional activity

Kilometres and miles
Pupils might investigate the relationship between kilometres and miles and compare continental speed limits (km/h) with speed limits in Britain (mph).

Equipment

None.

SM4c/7

MD/D1
MD/E1
ME/D1
T/D1, 2
PFS/E3
E+

Content

- Measurement to the nearest $\frac{1}{2}$ cm
- Use of scale to calculate true distances
- Calculation of
  - distance given time and speed
  - time given distance and speed
- Duration of time using 24-hour notation.

Detailed notes

| Q1 | Measurements on the map should be rounded to the nearest $\frac{1}{2}$ cm giving true distances to the nearest 25 km. |

| Q3 | Because so many different factors can affect sailing and flight times it is not possible to say exactly how long a journey will take. Hence the wording 'How long should it take . . . ?' |

| Q8b | As this trip takes several days pupils should also give the *day* of arriving back. |

Additional activity

Planning a trip
Pupils could plan, say, a five-day tour starting and finishing at the school and including visits to a number of places of interest. Consideration should be given to

- daily maximum travel distance
- distances between places of interest
- balance between time spent travelling and visiting
- choosing suitable locations for overnight stops, and so on.

Equipment

Ruler.
For the Additional activity: map showing distances between towns.

137	138	139	140
$x + a = b$	$x - a = b,$ $ax = b$	Mixed	Inequalities and inequations

E37	E38
Forming inequations	Systems of inequations

CONTENT AND DEVELOPMENT

Core

The inequality symbols $<$ and $>$ are used in Heinemann Mathematics 7.

In Heinemann Mathematics 8 *Equations*, algebraic equations and the symbols $\geq$ and $\leq$ are introduced. This section covers:

- construction of algebraic expressions
- construction and informal solution of equations of the forms
  $x + a = b, x - a = b, ax = b$
- ordering numbers using the inequality symbols $<$ and $>$
- Construction and solution of inequations of the form $x \leq a, x \geq a, x < a, x > a$.

Pupils are introduced to the idea of using a mathematical model to represent a real-life situation. They must realise that forming the equation is important. No formal method of solving equations is expected at this stage.

Extension

E37 and E38 should be attempted on completion of the Core Textbook pages. New work includes

- construction and informal solution of inequations of the form $x \pm a > b, x \pm a < b$
- solution of a system of simple inequations in context.

National Curriculum (England and Wales)

A2a, 3acd

Mathematics 5–14 (Scotland)

PSE
RTN/D4
FE/E2
ME/D9
E+

EQUIPMENT

Calculator.

For the Introductory activities: bag and 17 marbles, box of pencils/books or similar, a copy of the *The Highway Code*.

A2a,
3acd/6

FE/E2
E+

Content

- Construction of algebraic expressions then equations
- Use of these expressions in the construction of equations
- Informal solution of equations of the form $x + a = b$.

The letter n is used throughout to represent the unknown numbers.

Introductory activity

The unknown number
Pupils should appreciate that
- a letter can be used to represent an unknown *number*.
- this number can be found when further information is given.

Ask two pupils to act out the scene at the top of Core Textbook page 137 and other similar scenes with sweets in a bag, pencils in a box, books in a carton and so on.
- Pupil A asks the class to guess how many marbles are in the bag.
- After several guesses it is agreed that the number is unknown – suppose we call this number n.
- Pupil B gives Pupil A three more marbles.
- Ask the class how many marbles Pupil A now has ($n + 3$).

The rest of the scene can be acted out *after* pupils have completed Q1. (If other expressions have been formed for sweets, pencils, books and so on, then these could also become equations if further information is given.)

Detailed notes

Q1 Class discussion of these questions may help to reinforce the concept and will ensure that all pupils have a correct list of expressions to use in Q2.

Panel above Q2 The other scenes suggested in the Introductory activity should also be discussed. A formal written method for solving equations is not expected. Solutions are to be found informally, for example $n + 3 = 17$ could be read as 'what number add 3 gives 17' leading to 14 as the unknown number.

Equipment

For the Introductory activity: bag and 17 marbles, box of pencils/books or similar.

A3acd/6

FE/E2
E+

Content

- Construction and informal solution of equations of the forms $x - a = b$ and $ax = b$.

Several different letters are used for the unknown number.

Detailed notes

Panel above Q1 Discussion of this and other similar examples should stress that
- different letters may be used for the unknown numbers
- solutions can be 'thought out' as before.

Panel above Q3 It may be necessary to remind pupils that $9r$ means $9 \times r$.

Equipment

None.

A3acd/6

FE/E2
E+

Content

- Construction and informal solution of equations of the forms $x + a = b$, $x - a = b$ and $ax = b$
- Construction and informal solution of equations based on the perimeter and area of geometrical shapes.

In some examples, pupils choose a letter to represent the unknown number.

Detailed notes

Q3 Some pupils may need to be reminded of the meaning of the words 'area' and 'perimeter'.

Q3a Pupils may need to be reminded that $t + t + t + t = 4t$ and so the equation can be formed as $4t = 36$.

Equipment

None.

Content

- Ordering numbers using the inequality symbols $<$ and $>$
- Construction and solution of inequations of the forms $x \leqslant a$, $x \geqslant a$, $x < a$, $x > a$.

Introductory activities

1 Revision of the symbols $<$ and $>$
A number line could be drawn and a value, say 4, drawn on the line. Class discussion should conclude that 'numbers to the left are less than 4' and 'numbers to the right are greater than 4'.

The symbols $<$ and $>$ are a useful shorthand, for example, $1 < 4$, $7 > 4$.

Pupils could be asked to suggest ways of remembering the meanings of these symbols, for example,

- Each symbol looks like an arrowhead and always points to the smaller number
- $<$ looks like the letter L for Less than
- Each of the symbols $<$ and $>$ can be made by narrowing one end and widening the other end of the symbol $=$. The number at the narrow end is always the smaller number.

2 The symbols $\leqslant$ and $\geqslant$
A variety of signs could be chosen from *The Highway Code* to illustrate the various types of inequations, leading to the introduction of the symbols $\leqslant$ and $\geqslant$.

Detailed notes

Q1 Pupils who find the ordering of decimals difficult should locate each pair of values on the number line.

Q4 Pupils may need to be reminded that only the whole numbers from 0 to 9 should be considered.

Equipment

For Introductory activity 2: a copy of *The Highway Code*.

140
Equations:
Inequalities
and
inequations

A3acd/
$6 \rightarrow 7$

RTN/D4
FE/E2
E+

Content

- Construction of inequations using the symbols $<$, $>$, $\leqslant$, $\geqslant$
- Construction and informal solution of inequations of the form $x \pm a > b$, $x \pm a < b$.

Detailed notes

Q2 The phrases 'no more than' and 'at least' may need some discussion.

Panel above Q3 This type of inequation is not included in the work of the Core. The informal approach for equations described in the notes for Core Textbook page 137 should be used.

Equipment

None.

E37
Equations:
Forming
inequations

A3acd/6

FE/E2
ME/D9
E+

Content

- Interpretation of information in visual and symbolic form
- Calculation of time given distance and speed in mph.

Pupils use problem-solving strategies such as Working systematically and Reasoning to solve a simple system of inequations based on height and width restrictions for lorries using different routes.

Introductory activity

Road restrictions
Ask pupils if they have seen the police escorting a large load. What was the lorry carrying? Why are some roads not suitable for particular loads? (For example height, width, weight, length or turning circle of the load may be too great.)

Detailed notes

Q3b Either route could be chosen depending on the reason given. However, the shorter route is more likely to be chosen.

Q5 The informal methods used in the *Speed* section, Core Textbook pages 135 and 136, should be used.

Equipment

Calculator.

E38
Equations:
Systems of
inequations

A3acd/
$6 \rightarrow 7$

PSE
FE/E2
ME/D9
E+

142	143 W39 144	145 W40	146
Concept	Ordering; inequalities Inequations; addition and subtraction	Coordinates	Coordinates

E34, 35	E36
Addition, Subtraction	Equations with negatives

CONTENT AND DEVELOPMENT

Core

Heinemann Mathematics 7 contains work on the concept, language and recording of negative numbers which are displayed on both vertical and horizontal number lines.

Heinemann Mathematics 8 consolidates and develops these ideas and introduces the four-quadrant coordinate diagram, and includes:

- use of vertical and horizontal number lines to show integers
- informal addition and subtraction
- ordering integers using the symbols $>$ and $<$
- completion of sequences of integers on a number line
- listing solution sets of inequations of the forms $x > a$ and $x < b$
- reading and plotting points in all four quadrants
- construction and identification of 2D shapes
- informal translation of shapes in all four quadrants.

Extension

E34–E36 should be attempted on completion of the Core Textbook pages. E36 contains new work on the construction and informal solution of equations using integers.

National Curriculum (England and Wales)

N2b, 3c
A3bcd
SM3a

Mathematics 5–14 (Scotland)

PSE
RTN/E1
AS/E4
FE/E2
RS/E2
PM/E2
S/E2
E+

RELATED ACTIVITIES

Negative numbers in use
Pupils should try to find examples of negative numbers in everyday life. For example, weather charts, freezer indicators, scales on stereo equipment, golf scores (below par) and so on.

EQUIPMENT

Dice (2 colours), counters, $\frac{1}{2}$ cm and 1 cm squared paper, tracing paper.

For the Introductory activities: prepared OHP transparencies.

Content

- Use of vertical and horizontal number lines to show integers
- Informal addition and subtraction based on movement on a number line.

Introductory activities

In both activities language, positive and negative, and notation $+5$ and -5 should be stressed, including the positioning of the negative symbol.

1 Vertical number line
A large thermometer scale could be drawn and used to illustrate rises and falls of temperature from different starting values.

2 Horizontal number line
A stereo treble or bass sliding control could be drawn and used to show increases and decreases from different starting settings.

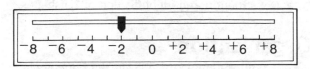

Equipment

None.

Content

- Completion of sequences of integers on number lines
- Ordering integers using the inequality symbols $>$ and $<$
- Listing solution sets of inequations of the forms $x > a$ and $x < b$
- Addition and subtraction of a whole number to and from an integer.

Organisation

Q1 and Q10 require pupils to work in pairs.

Detailed notes

Q1 Some pupils may need help to interpret the instructions for the game, called 'Lucky Thirteen'. The game should be played several times. The fact that -13 is more likely than 13 could be discussed after the game has been played.

W39, Q2 The number lines should be completed before the answer boxes.

W39, Q3 Pupils may need to be reminded to choose from the given set.

Q8, 9 Pupils may use the 'Lucky Thirteen' number strip or draw a number line of their own. Those having difficulty could spend more time playing 'Lucky Thirteen'.

Q10 This game provides valuable experience of integers and should be played several times.

Additional activities

Addition and subtraction
Further examples of addition and subtraction could be supplied. More able pupils may cope with more than 2 integers and a wider range of integers, for example:

- $-5 + 3 - 6$ ■ $6 - 14 - 8$
- $-9 + 25 - 17$ ■ $-34 - 16 + 28$

Equipment

Dice (2 colours), counters.

143
144
W39
Negative numbers: Ordering; inequalities Inequations; addition and subtraction

N2b, 3c/5

RTN/E1
FE/E2
AS/E4

145
W40
Negative
numbers:
Coordinates

N2b, 3c/5
SM3a/5
RTN/E1
RS/E2
PM/E2

Content

- Use of the terms *x*-axis, *y*-axis, origin, *x*-coordinate, *y*-coordinate
- Plotting and reading points in four quadrants
- Construction and identification of 2D shapes.

Organisation

Pupils should attempt Q1 to Q5 after Introductory activity 1. Introductory activity 2 refers to Q6 and Q7.

Introductory activities

1 Four quadrant coordinates
It may be beneficial to revise first quadrant coordinates including

- the name and numbering of each axis
- the name and coordinates of the origin
- the plotting of points, for example, A(2, 6), B(4, 0), C(0, 5), D(4, 6)
- the points which lie on the *x*-axis
- the points which lie on the *y*-axis.

Thereafter each axis should be extended as a number line to make a four quadrant diagram and a similar discussion to the above could take place using K(4, 6), L($^-$2, 3), M($^-$3, $^-$6), N(5, $^-$6), P(0, 3), Q(4, 0), R($^-$3, 0), S(0, $^-$5).

2 x- and y-coordinates
Emphasise the individual coordinates by discussing

- the *x*-coordinate and the *y*-coordinate of each point
- the *x*-coordinate of points on the *y*-axis
- the points with the same *x*-coordinate
- the *y*-coordinate of points on the *x*-axis
- the points with the same *y*-coordinate.

Detailed notes

| Q5c | The different possible answers, including the V-kite, should be discussed. |

| W40, Q2 | The cyclic order of the points is shown by the arrows. Encourage pupils to join the points one by one as they are plotted. |

Additional activities

1 Battleships
This game, and others like it, could be used to give practice in reading and plotting points in all four quadrants.

2 Shapes
Pupils could make their own shapes, similar to those in W40, Q2, and give the coordinates of the vertices to a partner who should then plot the points and reproduce the shapes.

Equipment

$\frac{1}{2}$ cm or 1 cm squared paper.

146
Negative
numbers:
Coordinates

SM3a/5
PSE
RTN/E1
PM/E2

Content

- Reading and plotting points in four quadrants.

Pupils use strategies such as Working systematically and Elimination to solve problems in the context of a treasure island.

Detailed notes

| Map above Q1 | Some pupils may need help to interpret the clues given beside the map. |

| Q4 | Emphasise that it is the origin on the tracing paper which is moved to each point in turn. A demonstration may be useful. |

Additional activity

Make a picture
Pupils could make a picture similar to that in Q3 and give the coordinates of the vertices to a partner who should then plot the points to reproduce the picture. More able pupils could attempt a picture similar to the one in Q4.

Equipment

Tracing paper, $\frac{1}{2}$ cm and 1 cm squared paper.

Content

- Informal translation of shapes in four quadrants
- Addition and subtraction of a whole number to and from an integer.

Organisation

Introductory activity 1 refers to the work on E34.
Introductory activity 2 refers to the work on E35.

Introductory activities

1 Moving right
It may be necessary to provide some help by discussing examples similar to Q1 to Q4.
Emphasise that
- the *y*-coordinate is unchanged,
- the *x*-coordinate increases by the same number of units which the shape moves.

2 Moving left
Repeat Introductory activity 1 for the shapes moving left.

Detailed notes

E34, Q1 The small shapes – circle, cross and square – are used to represent the vertices and the letters P, Q, R indicate the different positions of the triangle on the coordinate diagram.

E34, Q7 Pupils may need to copy the square and draw its new positions. Tracing paper may be useful.

E34, Q7b Some pupils may not realise that the square moves 8 units from its original position.

E35, Q7 Pupils may need to copy the parallelogram and draw its new positions. Tracing paper may be useful.

Equipment

Tracing paper, $\frac{1}{2}$ cm or 1 cm squared paper. For the Introductory activities: prepared OHP transparencies of four quadrant diagrams.

E34
E35
Negative numbers: Addition, Subtraction

N3c/5
SM3a/5

RTN/E1
AS/E4
PM/E2
S/E2
E+

Content

- Construction and informal solution of equations of the forms $x \pm a = b$ using integers.

Detailed notes

Q1 Pupils may be tempted to find the unknown temperatures without first forming the equations. However, it is important that the work of this page is seen to be about using mathematical models (forming equations) to represent real-life situations, as well as solving equations with negative numbers.

Equipment

None.

E36
Negative numbers: Equations with negatives

N3c/5
A3bcd/6

PSE
RTN/E1
FE/E2
E+

147 148	149 W41	150	151	152 W42	153 W43 W44	154	155 W45
Planning the holiday/flights	Plane spotting, Scale drawing	Runways	Loading and fuelling	Take-off	In flight	Sydney International Airport	Touchdown

CONTENT AND DEVELOPMENT

Core

This is the second 'extended context' in Heinemann Mathematics 8. General advice concerning the purpose of and the management of an 'extended context' can be found on page T6 of these notes.

Flight to Australia simulates events which occur when the Johnston family travel to Sydney at the start of their holiday. Activities revolve around

- planning the holiday
- aircraft and preparation for take-off at London Heathrow
- the flight itself and a near-miss on arrival at Sydney International Airport.

The mathematical content includes:

- interpretation of information in written, visual and tabular form
- recognition of sequence in number and time
- matching photographs of aircraft to their plans or elevations
- interpretation and construction of scale drawings, and calculations involving scale
- problems using compound measures and relationships between units
- measurement of angles to 1°
- use of compass points and three-figure bearings to specify directions
- recognition and extension of number pattern
- use of a formula to calculate height
- construction and interpretation of straight-line graphs
- investigation of seating arrangements.

National Curriculum (England and Wales)

UA2ac, 3abde
N3b
A2c, 3b
SM2ad, 3d, 4ac

Mathematics 5–14 (Scotland)

PSE	I/E1, 2	I/E
D/E1	M/E1	AS/D3
MD/D4	FPR/D1	PS/D1
PS/E	FE/D1	ME/D1, 9
T/D1, 2	PFS/E3	RS/D
PM/D1, 2	PM/E1, 3	A/D2
A/E	E+	

RELATED ACTIVITIES

Travelling by air
It may be possible to arrange a visit to a travel agent or an airport. Some Air Traffic Control units are prepared to show small groups around their establishments. This would give first-hand experience of the problems simulated on the pages.

Other aspects of foreign travel, for example time zones, could be investigated. Possible links with work in geography could be explored.

EQUIPMENT

Calculator, ruler, protractor, $\frac{1}{2}$ cm squared paper, coloured pencils.

For the Introductory and Additional activities: holiday brochures.

Content

- Interpretation of information in tabular form including timetables
- Addition of up to four-digit whole numbers
- Recognition of sequences in number and time.

The calculations involve distances in kilometres, currency in pounds sterling and Australian dollars and durations of time using 24-hour notation. A problem solving task is included which requires pupils to work methodically.

Introductory activities

1 Introduction to the flight to Australia
To set the scene for the whole context class discussion should cover important features such as:

- booking a holiday through a travel agent
- airports, aircraft and air travel.

2 Holiday brochures
Pupils could look at extracts from these to practise interpretation of tables. When are the cheapest rates? What is the most expensive time to travel? Can you think of a reason for this?

Detailed notes

147, Q8b If preferred, some pupils may use the current exchange rate as quoted in the daily press.

148, Q4 Ensure pupils realise that S stands for Saturday, since Su is used for Sunday.

Additional activity

The family holiday
Pupils could choose and cost a holiday from a brochure.

Equipment

Calculator.
For the Introductory and Additional activities: holiday brochures.

147
148
Extended context 2: Planning the holiday/flight

UA2a, 3d/6
SM4a/5

PSE
I/E1
M/E1
AS/D3
PS/E
T/D1, 2

Content

- Interpretation of information in visual form
- Matching photographs of aircraft to their plans or elevations
- Interpretation and construction of a scale drawing with given scales.

Introductory activity

Jumbo drawings
It may be helpful to discuss the fact that the three drawings on W41 are to the same scale, 1 cm to 10 m, although the scale is expressed in different ways.

Detailed notes

Q1 Each of the six photographs at the top of Core Textbook page 149 matches one of the diagrams at the bottom of the page. Some guidance on how to write answers may be necessary, for example, A3, B1, and so on. Pupils could work in groups before a whole-class discussion takes place.

W41, Q1 The scale has been 'doubled' by using 1 cm squares instead of the $\frac{1}{2}$ cm squares of the original and so the drawing can be completed square by square. Pupils should not be expected to produce 'perfect' diagrams.

W41, Q2, Q3 The scale line applies to both drawings. The actual length and wingspan can be found directly from the diagram but a ruler will be needed for the heights.

Equipment

Ruler.

149
W41
Extended context 2: Plane spotting Scale drawings

SM2a/6

PSE
I/E1
PFS/E3
RS/D

150
Extended
context 2:
Runways

SM2d,
3d/5
I/E
FPR/D1
ME/D1
PFS/E3
A/E

Content

- Interpretation of a map and following directional instructions
- Calculations involving scale, metre/kilometre relationship
- Measurement of angles.

Introductory activity

Map work

A real map of Heathrow Airport or the nearest major airport to the school will show many interesting features which do not appear in this simplified version on the Core Textbook page 150. General discussion might involve questions such as:
'Why were the runways built in these directions?'
'Why three runways?'
'Are the various facilities in the best positions?'
and so on.

Equipment

Ruler, protractor.

Detailed notes

Q2, Q3 The measurements which pupils have to take from the map are whole numbers of centimetres.

Q5 The map distance from P to Q is 5·5 cm.

Q6 Some pupils may need guidance to decide where to measure when finding the distance between two parallel lines.

Q9, Q10 Pupils might be tempted to give the supplements of the angles asked for.

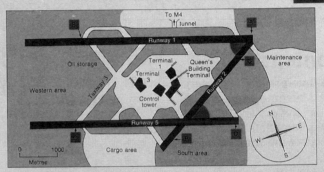

Runways 150
Extended context

This is a simplified map of Heathrow Airport.

1 The scale on the map shows that 2 cm represents 1000 m. What does 1 cm represent?

2 (a) Measure the length of Runway 1 from A to B in centimetres.
  (b) Calculate the true length from A to B in metres.

3 Find the **full** length of Runway 1 in (a) metres (b) kilometres.

4 A plane starts at A, travels $\frac{2}{3}$ of the full length of Runway 1 and then takes off. What length of runway did it not use?

5 A plane touches down at P on Runway 2 and stops at Q. What is its landing distance in metres?

6 How far apart, in kilometres, are Runway 1 and Runway 5?

7 Measure the size of the red angle
  (a) between Runway 2 and Runway 5
  (b) between Runway 2 and Runway 1.

8 Find **both** angles which Taxiway 3 makes with Runway 5.

9 A Jumbo touches down on Runway 5 at C and travels to D. It turns left to taxi towards the Queen's Building Terminal. What angle does the nose of the aircraft swing through to make the turn?

10 An A300 Airbus taxies out from Terminal 3 towards B and turns left on to Runway 1. What size of angle does it turn through?

Content

- Addition, subtraction and multiplication problems using weight in kg and tonnes
- Problems using rates including kilograms per person, tonnes per minute, tonnes per hour and miles per hour.

Introductory activity

Loading a jumbo
Some discussion of the complex procedures followed when preparing a jumbo for flight would be helpful to set the scene, for example, the safety aspects of maximum weights, referring to the information at the top of the page, and the need to jettison fuel in an emergency.

Detailed notes

Q2a	Some pupils may need to be reminded that 1000 kg = 1 tonne.

Equipment

None.

151
Extended
context 2:
Loading and
fuelling

N3b/5
SM4c/7

AS/D3
MD/D4
E+

Content

- Interpretation of information in written and visual form
- Use of compass points to specify directions
- Scale drawing including angles to 1 degree
- Compound measures
- Relationship between temperature in °C and height in metres.

Introductory activity

The windsock
Class discussion should highlight and explain the key ideas of windsocks. A bird's-eye view indicates wind direction and a side view gives some indication of wind strength.

Detailed notes

Panel above Q1	This may need careful explanation, stressing that the windsock is viewed from *above*. Pupils need to know that a NW wind blows **from** the **NW**.
Photo-graph above Q3	Pupils should understand that this is the side view of the windsock. Some discussion may be necessary to highlight the relationship between the angle of the windsock and the wind speed.
W42, Q4	The idea of 'distance along the ground' may need discussion.
W42, Q5	Pupils could be asked to draw a graph to display the information in the completed table.

Additional activity

Improvised windsock
Ask pupils to design and construct a device to measure wind speed.

Equipment

Ruler, protractor.

152
W42
Extended
context 2:
Take-off

UA3d/5

I/E2
D/E1
ME/D1, 9
PM/D1, 2
PFS/E3
A/E
E+

153
W43
W44
Extended
context 2:
In flight

UA2c,
3e/6

PSE
PS/D1
FE/D1

Content

- Interpretation of information in written and visual form
- Recognition and extension of number patterns.

Introductory activity

Seating arrangements
Classroom furniture could be set up to demonstrate seating plans and help clarify the meaning of 'disturbance factor'.

Detailed notes

`Q2c` Pupils may be unsure what a 'disturbance factor' of 0 means.

`W44`
- There are other possible positions for the passages in 9- and 10-seat rows.
- 'Symmetrical' seat arrangements such as 1–6–2 and 2–6–1 have the same 'disturbance factor'.
- Extreme arrangements such as 1–8–1 or 4–1–5 give large 'disturbance factors'.

`Q4, Q5` Encourage a systematic approach in which extremes are avoided.

Additional activity

Report
Pupils could write a brief report about their investigation summarising their findings and generalising as far as possible. The reports could be discussed and displayed.

Equipment

$\frac{1}{2}$ cm squared paper.

154
Extended
context 2:
Sydney
International
Airport

UA3ad/5

I/E1
PFS/E3
PM/D1
PM/E3
A/D2

Content

- Interpretation of information on a radar screen
- Use of three-figure bearings and compass directions.

Detailed notes

`Radar screen above Q1` Discuss this diagram to ensure that pupils understand
- the relationship between compass directions and three-figure bearings
- the airport is at the centre of the screen
- the concentric circles are 1 cm apart.
Some pupils may be able to describe radar screens they have seen in films.

`Q4` Aircraft 'between' circles should be taken to be exactly half way between them.
`Q6` A ruler laid across the diagram may help some pupils to determine the direction.

Equipment

None.

155
W45
Extended
context 2:
Touchdown

UA3b/6
A2c, 3b/6

PSE
I/E1, 2
D/E1
PFS/E3
PM/E1, 3
A/D2
E+

Content

- Use of a formula to calculate height
- Construction and interpretation of a straight-line graph
- Use of three-figure bearings, compass directions and simple scale
- Interpretation of information in written and tabular form.

Detailed notes

`Q1` It may be necessary to stress that the time is measured from the moment the jumbo is cleared to land.
`Q3d` It may be necessary to point out that the time 0654 corresponds to the time 0 on the time axis.

Equipment

Ruler, $\frac{1}{2}$ cm squared paper, coloured pencils.

DETOURS IN PART 4

General advice about using the Detours can be found on page T6 of these Notes.

126
W38
Detour: Approximation to one significant figure

N3f/6 → 7

RTN/D4
MD/D1
MD/E1, 4
AS/D1
RN/D1
PM/D3

Content

- Rounding to the nearest 1, 10 and 100
- Approximate calculations in money using prices rounded 'to one significant figure'
- Plotting points on a coordinate diagram.

Introductory activities

1 Rounding
Pupils need not be introduced to the language 'round to *x* significant figures' since it is not used in the questions. It may be helpful for some pupils to revise 'rounding to the nearest unit, 10 and 100' as in the following example for rounding 37 to the nearest 10.

- Draw a number line showing 30 and 40.

```
30                    40
|────────────────────|
```

- Find the number midway between 30 and 40 and position it on the line.

```
30        35        40
|─────────|─────────|
```

- The number 37 is then positioned and can be seen to be nearer 40 than 30.
37 is '40 to the nearest ten'.

```
                  37
30        35       ↓  40
|─────────|───────────|
```

2 Is it nearer?
Using prices from adverts, a discussion based on the question 'Is it nearer?' could be useful to revise rounding to the nearest £1, £10 and £100. Examples could include rounding, say £8·50, to nearest £1 giving £8 or £9. This would give an opportunity to emphasise that the context often determines how the rounding should be carried out.

Equipment
Calculator.

Detailed notes

Q3 The instructions for rounding may need further explanation.

W38, Q1 The worked example shows both figures being rounded down. Pupils should realise that this does not happen in every example.

W38, Q2 A calculator should be used. The use of approximate calculations as a check on calculator work should be discussed.

W38, Q3 The first point '**a**' is marked with a cross. An eye is also drawn which becomes part of the final picture.

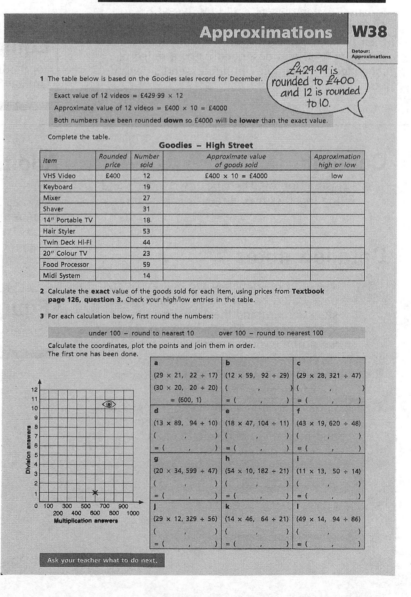

Approximations — W38

Detour: Approximations

£429·99 is rounded to £400 and 12 is rounded to 10.

1 The table below is based on the Goodies sales record for December.

Exact value of 12 videos = £429·99 × 12

Approximate value of 12 videos = £400 × 10 = £4000

Both numbers have been rounded **down** so £4000 will be **lower** than the exact value.

Complete the table.

Goodies – High Street

Item	Rounded price	Number sold	Approximate value of goods sold	Approximation high or low
VHS Video	£400	12	£400 × 10 = £4000	low
Keyboard		19		
Mixer		27		
Shaver		31		
14″ Portable TV		18		
Hair Styler		53		
Twin Deck Hi-Fi		44		
20″ Colour TV		23		
Food Processor		59		
Midi System		14		

2 Calculate the **exact** value of the goods sold for each item, using prices from **Textbook page 126, question 3.** Check your high/low entries in the table.

3 For each calculation below, first round the numbers:

under 100 – round to nearest 10   over 100 – round to nearest 100

Calculate the coordinates, plot the points and join them in order. The first one has been done.

a	b	c
(29 × 21, 22 ÷ 17)	(12 × 59, 92 ÷ 29)	(29 × 28, 321 ÷ 47)
(30 × 20, 20 ÷ 20)	(,)	(,)
= (600, 1)	= (,)	= (,)
d	**e**	**f**
(13 × 89, 94 ÷ 10)	(18 × 47, 104 ÷ 11)	(43 × 19, 620 ÷ 48)
(,)	(,)	(,)
= (,)	= (,)	= (,)
g	**h**	**i**
(20 × 34, 599 ÷ 47)	(54 × 10, 182 ÷ 21)	(11 × 13, 50 ÷ 14)
(,)	(,)	(,)
= (,)	= (,)	= (,)
j	**k**	**l**
(29 × 12, 329 ÷ 56)	(14 × 46, 64 ÷ 21)	(49 × 14, 94 ÷ 86)
(,)	(,)	(,)
= (,)	= (,)	= (,)

Ask your teacher what to do next.

141
Detour:
Matching
areas,
investigation

UA2ab,
4a/6
SM4d/6

PSE
I/E1
PFS/E3

Content

- Interpretation of information in written and visual forms
- Interpretation and construction of scale drawings
- Use of strategies such as Make a model, Trial and improvement and Reasoning.

Introductory activity

Moving carpets
In discussion pupils who have experienced moving house could be asked what was done to find out if carpets would fit the new house and what problems were met. For example:

- did the colours of the carpets suit every room
- was a join hidden under a piece of furniture acceptable, and so on?

Detailed notes

Notepad beside Q1–Q3 Discussion of these specific conditions would be valuable. Note that the plans on Core Textbook page 141 are not drawn exactly to scale.

Equipment

Scissors, $\frac{1}{2}$ cm squared paper.

S46
Detour:
Spatial
relationships

SM2a/4 → 5

PSE
RS/C3
RS/D

Content

- Interpretation of information in visual form
- Recognition, description and drawing of different outline views of 3D objects.

Introductory activity

What am I?
Small everyday objects could be placed on an OHP and pupils asked to try to identify them from their projected images. Different silhouetted views could be used and described using a range of language, for example, 'front/back/end/side/top/bottom'.

Detailed notes

Q1 Only one view of the gun is shown. Two views of each of the others are shown. Different words may be used to describe each outline view, for example front, back and end are all acceptable for the roller skate.

Equipment

For the Introductory activity: OHP, small familiar 3D objects.

S47
Detour:
Constructing
shapes

UA2abd/4

PSE
RS/D

Content

- Construction of 2D shapes by selecting and fitting together two, three, or four given shapes.

Detailed notes

First line The strip of shapes at the bottom of the page could be cut out as a single piece, stuck to card and then the separate shapes cut out. The thicker card shapes would be easier to work with.

Second line The shapes on the page match the cutouts in size. Pupils should build on top of the page shapes.

Q1 Pupils may find solutions to one problem when working on another. They may also find more than one solution to a particular problem.

Additional activity

Area
The shapes make up a square of side 4 cm with total area 16 cm². The areas of the four individual pieces could be calculated and used to work out the area of each new shape that is constructed.

Equipment

Scissors, card.

Content

- Interpretation of information in written and visual forms
- Recognition and extension of a number pattern
- Use of strategies such as the Trial and improvement, Look for a pattern and Reasoning.

Organisation

Although the rectangles theme applies throughout the work of the page there are two distinct activities each of which may require a separate introduction.

Detailed notes

Q1 The copied rectangles do not need to be accurate. However, the regions should be clearly defined by the lines.

Q4e The discussion should conclude that each new line should cross every old line avoiding existing intersections.

Additional activity

The four-colour theorem
Pupils could find out about this theorem using the library or other resources.

They could then try to apply it to a tracing of a map showing a number of regions, for example countries or counties.

Equipment

Coloured pencils; duplicated copies of the diagrams in Q1 would save recording time. For the Additional activity: atlas, tracing paper.

E29
Detour:
Colouring
maps
investigation

UA2cd, 4b/6

PSE
PS/D1
FE/D1

Content

- Interpretation of information in visual form
- Interpretation of a 2D representation of a 3D object
- Construction of a cube from a net.

Detailed notes

Q2 Pupils should notice that the sums for each row and column are the same but that the sums for the diagonals of the faces are different. The faces of the cube should not be confused with 'magic squares' which pupils may have met previously.

Q3 Pupils may find it helpful to construct a cube of edge 3 cm as described in Q4. They can insert missing numbers as they find them and then draw the faces from the completed cube.

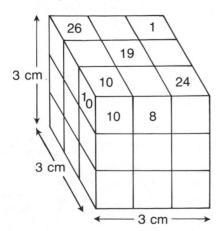

Q4 Pupils may find it useful to use isometric dot paper to draw the layers. Pupils answers may vary since they depend on the orientation of the cube.

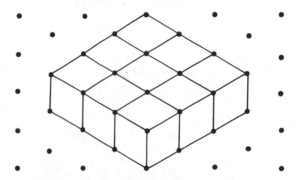

Additional activity

Sums for the axes
Pupils could investigate totals for sets of small cubes lying on axes passing through the central internal cube.

Equipment

Scissors, glue, 1 cm squared paper, 1 cm isometric dot paper.

E32
Detour:
Number
investigation

UA2abd, 3bd/6

PSE
AS/D1
RS/D1, 6